CHOROLOGICAL DIFFERENTIATION

AS THE FUNDAMENTAL PRINCIPLE
OF GEOGRAPHY

AN INQUIRY INTO
THE CHOROLOGICAL CONCEPTION
OF GEOGRAPHY

Dr. G. DE JONG

ORD. PROFESSOR IN THE FREE UNIVERSITY
AT AMSTERDAM

J. B. WOLTERS - GRONINGEN - 1962

PREFACE

On the publication of this study it is proper for me to express my sincere gratitude to the 'Nederlandse Organisatie voor Zuiver-Wetenschappelijk Onderzoek' * for having undertaken to bear the expenses of both, translation and publication.

The translation has been done by Mr. H. de Jongste, Rotterdam. I thank him for taking the trouble to make himself conversant with the subject-matter, and for his devotion to his task.

Thanks are also due to Mr. P. L. H. Feschotte, assistant for Economic Geography at the Free University, Amsterdam, for his painstaking assistance in the revision of this translation and in correcting the proof-sheets.

And finally I would like to say something about the quotations inserted in this study. In English-speaking countries it is becoming more and more usual to give an English translation of the passages quoted from foreign authors. There are, of course, objections to be raised against this procedure, as these translations are then no longer quotations in the proper sense of the word. As, however, this study appears in English, we have decided after some hesitation to translate the German quotations together with one from a French author. In many cases, however, we have added certain German words and sentence parts between brackets. In connection with the specifically German terminology it was sometimes impossible to render certain German words and concepts in English. In such a case they have been left untranslated.

* Netherlands Organization for the Advancement of Pure Research (Z.W.O.).

III

CONTENTS

		Page
	Preface	III
I.	Introduction	1
II.	Chorological Differentiation and Region	10
III.	Analysis of the Vertical Chorological Complex . . .	26
IV.	Geotopes and Vertical Chorological Unities	64
V.	Unities of Vertical Interrelation and Horizontal Inter-connection as the Basis of Chorological Differentiation	75
VI.	Chorological Differentiation and Interconnection versus Historical Change and Development	99
VII.	The General and the Special within Chorological Differentiation	140
VIII.	Summary	190
	Notes	199
	References	209

CHAPTER I

INTRODUCTION

When the chorological principle of geography is mentioned, many people will think of the great German geographer Hettner, who in his writings has given an elaborate and thorough-going exposition of this principle and this conception. We are further reminded of the views of von Humboldt, Ritter, and von Richthofen, who already before that time had advanced certain ideas implied in the chorological principle. We also involuntarily think of the philosopher Immanuel Kant, who in his lectures laid the foundations of geography as a chorological science. And finally in our time we direct our thoughts to Hartshorne, who has elucidated the chorological idea in his monumental book "The Nature of Geography".

Though these prominent figures stand out at once, it would be wrong if we should not immediately add to them the names of many geographers in Germany, Switzerland, Belgium, the United States, Russia and Japan, who have propagated the chorological idea and applied it in their works, using especially Hettner's theoretical work as a basis.

As is indicated by the title of our study we wish to make an investigation into the conception of chorological differentiation. This differentiation is a further specialization of the chorological principle. The chorological principle is the very general principle of geography. Although presently we shall explain why in our opinion the concept chorological should be preferred to the concept spatial in geography, we shall employ also the more usual term spatial in this short introductory elucidation of the subject of our inquiry.

So we concentrate our attention on the spatial aspect, the spatial principle in spatial differentiation. In our opinion this is the fundamental principle of the chorological conception.

Hettner says: "Geography is the science of the spatial arrangement (Anordnung) on the earth surface" [1]. He opposes geographical sciences to historical sciences, "which owe their unity to the viewpoint of the temporal process (zeitlichen Ablaufes) of things" [2].

1

Two circumstances are decisive of the spatial arrangement of things: "The one is the difference between one locality and another with the spatial interconnections of juxtapositional things. Not any phenomenon of the earth surface can be considered in itself, it is always exclusively intelligible in the comprehension of its relative location with respect to other earth spaces. The second circumstance is the causal interrelation of the different kingdoms of nature (Naturreiche) and their different phenomena united in one place" [3].

Hettner opposes spatial differentiation to historical diversity or the differentiation of the phenomena of different times (periods). The spatial interconnection of the various places of the earth surface has its counter instance in the interconnection of the different periods of time and in the development of history. Geography and history approach each other in the interrelation of the different things and their phenomena in one place and the interrelation of the different things and phenomena at one definite time [4].

Hettner then opposes geography and history both to the systematic sciences. The latter "leave temporal and local relations in the background and find their unity in the similarity or affinity of the things with which they occupy themselves" [5].

We shall not go into details with respect to the way in which Hettner combines both astronomy as the spatial science of the world (universe) and geography as the spatial science of the earth surface with the historical sciences and the systematic sciences as concrete theoretical empirical sciences in opposition to the abstract theoretical empirical sciences [6].

Although in our opinion the distinction between concrete and abstract empirical sciences borrowed from Comte can be formally criticized, we do not wish to pass judgment on it, because we are not competent to do so on account of our insufficient knowledge of the philosophy of the sciences.

But Hettner's idea of geography as a chorological science is our starting-point. In our study this principle is not a thesis but a theme. Geography as a science, however complicated it may be, is intelligible to us only from the chorological conception, in which the chorological differentiation is the fundamental element.

Geography, therefore, deals with the spatial differentiation of a totality of things and their phenomena. Things and phenomena are interrelated in one locality, they form a spatial totality, a spatial complex [7]. Owing to the relative location of the different places of the earth surface the things and phenomena of different places are also connected with each other by all kinds of spatial relations. As to the latter we would observe that it is precisely the spatial differentiation of things and phenomena which forms an important condition of the spatial interconnections of the various localities. No doubt the latter are based on their relative location. But this location will be of special importance when the things of a diversity of localities display mutual differences.

For this reason we are of opinion that the principle of chorological differentiation is the most important element of the chorological idea.

Ritters says: "The geographical sciences are preferably concerned with the spaces of the earth surface in so far as the latter are filled terrestrially (to whatever natural kingdom they may belong and whatever forms they may have been given)..." [8]. He does not emphasize differentiation. Ritter lays the stress on the interrelation of things in one locality and on the spatial interconnection of different localities. Especially the latter, viz., relative location, draws Ritter's attention [9].

It is clear, however, that there can be no question of spaces if one space is not distinct from another. If there was no difference, there would be only one space, one uniform earth surface. It is exactly the spatial differences the earth surface really displays which give rise to the existence of separate spaces. These spatial differences are the basis of the indication of the separate spaces. Besides, as has already been observed, spatial differentiation is an active factor in the spatial relations of the different localities.

In our opinion it is no wonder, therefore, that in answer to a statement made by von Richthofen, who circumscribes geography as the science of the earth surface, Hettner says: "Views of the earth surface in its entirety, i.e., without regard to local differences, are not geographical, for geography is much rather the science of the earth surface according to its local differences, of the parts of

3

the world, countries, landscapes, and localities" [10]. Or, as he puts it in another work of his: "The object of geography is the diversity of the earth surface to be found in all the natural kingdoms and in mankind" [11].

However, the spatial interconnections of the things of various places, their relative locations, are a very important factor in Hettner's system. Chorological differentiation, however, is a primary concern with him, and in our opinion rightly so.

Hartshorne, who in his last book also lays the stress on spatial differentiation, speaks of *variation*. He says: "Similarity, ... is not the opposite of difference but merely a generalization under which differences deemed minor are ignored, those deemed major are emphasized. Some writers seek to avoid misunderstanding by speaking always of differences and similarities, without recognising that the phrase is redundant. It may well be also that the repeated use of the term *differences* gives undue emphasis to the search for contrasts. It therefore seems advisable to use the more neutral word variations" [12].

Although we partly subscribe to his reasoning, we do not wish to follow him in his replacing the term differentiation by the word variation. We shall occasionally use both terms for stylistic reasons, but we prefer the word differentiation. Both terms refer to the divergence of a whole into parts. In the chorological or spatial differentiation the unity as well as the difference (not the opposition) between the regions are important. Every region is a speciality and at the same time a reflection of the earth surface as a whole. To distinguish regions it is necessary to pay attention to their differences. Otherwise regions are indistinguishable. Except for these differences there would be no question of regions and they could not be indicated and described. To our mind the concept *differentiation* expresses the difference better, and at the same time it implies the idea of the unity of the regions.

But the term differentiation confronts us with technical difficulties, although the same thing applies to the word variation.

In a literal sense differentiation connotes the process of differentiating, but the word is also used for its result.

4

We speak of the chorological differentiation of earthly things, e.g. of the soil, and of the chorological differentiation of the earth surface. The result of this differentiation is a sea clay soil, a low peat soil, etc., and we say that the earth surface differentiates into regions. However, we also say that this result, the sea clay soil, is a chorological differentiation of the soil, and that a region is a chorological differentiation of the earth surface.

In our study the term differentiation is used in both meanings, and the context will usually at once reveal in which sense the word differentiation is to be taken.

But in special cases, when we want to lay emphasis on the fact that the result of the differentiating process is meant, we have introduced the unusual word chorological *"differentiant"*. This expression is especially used to denote a particular region as distinct from other regions.

A region owes its existence to the chorological differentiation of the earth surface, it is the result of the chorological differentiation of terrestrial things and their phenomena. A region conceived of as a whole distinct from other regions, is called a chorological differentiant, if the finer chorological differentiation within it is ignored.

A differentiant is therefore a differentiation in the sense of the result of the differentiating process.

The spatial or chorological principle, and in particular chorological differentiation, is a foundational principle to many geographers. It would apparently be possible to speak of a movement in geography which purposely advocates this conception. We would even go further and say: In the course of its development geographical science has always consciously, or partly unconsciously, accepted the principle of chorological differentiation as its starting-point. This view, viz., that chorological differentiation is a conception which has revealed itself in the different geographical sciences through the ages, and that this idea is the key-note of the various geographical ways of thought, is the reason why we wish to subject this principle to a further systematic investigation.

The idea mentioned is a conviction which is not further examined in the present study. To do so would necessitate an

5

elaborate and very comprehensive critical historical inquiry.

To show that our view is not an unfounded casual thought, but a conviction, we will demonstrate in this introduction with an example that even those geographers that combat Hettner, accept the basic idea of chorological differentiation on which Hettner founded his system.

We are referring to the Utrecht social geography, which is so very important in the Netherlands.

The Utrecht School has in the first instance based itself on the work of the French geographers Vidal de la Blache and Brunhes. The activities of these two great scientists in the early part of the twentieth century are considered by the Utrecht geographers to be a turning point in the development of human geography. In connection with this, people sometimes speak of a Copernican revolution [13].

Although we have some knowledge of the ideas of the two French geographers, we prefer to found our observations on the pronouncements made by others, who have made a special study of the views of these two founders of modern French human geography. We shall therefore restrict ourselves to the Utrecht geographers [14], and here in particular to Cools' oration, which gives a concise and clear survey of the ideas of Vidal and Brunhes.

In their study of the phenomena on the earth surface proceeding from the relation between man and nature, between a social group and a physical environment, French human geography has strongly opposed certain German geographers who in their study of these phenomena laid emphasis on nature, on the physical environment, and who often considered this environment as the determining factor of the human phenomena. Brunhes and Vidal de la Blache, on the other hand, state that the activities of man and of the social group are of primary importance.

Brunhes mentioned the various possibilities offered by nature. Vidal considered the action of the human group in its adaptation to the conditions of life obtaining in a particular environment, and in a victory over the obstacles put in the way of such a group by this environment. He also opposes possibilism to determinism. Whereas Brunhes looked on a cultivated landscape as the source of the knowledge of human activity and of the way of life, to Vidal de la

Blache the "genre de vie", the group's attitude to life in relation to its environment — not this environment in itself — was the key to the explanation of the way of life of the group in its living space.

These thoughts are important. In the struggle against physical determinism the emphasis was especially laid on the *general* significance of active man in the relation of man to nature. The fact that Brunhes and Vidal de la Blache analyse the relation between man and nature, and approach the phenomena proceeding from it psychologically and sociologically, assigning a central position to human attitudes and actions, is very important and an advance in geographical research.

But in their works the two geographers discuss *different* cultivated landscapes, a *different* "genre de vie", *different* ways of living in *different* living spaces. Ultimately they are not concerned with that which the cultivated landscapes and the "genre de vie" of nations and human groups, the productive processes and the ways of life have in common, but with the chorological differentiation of these things.

The spatial differentiation of the relation between man and nature and its phenomena, such as "genre de vie", way of life and form of subsistence, pursuit of prosperity, productive process and other phenomena, leads to different earth spaces, countries, areas, and regions. Earth spaces are formed by the spatial differentiation of a totality of the phenomena of man and nature. In them the differentiation is insolubly connected with the spatial, for there is no possibility of a separate space if it is not distinct from other spaces.

Vidal expresses this very emphatically: "Geography is the science of *localities* and not of men" [15]. In the introduction to his "Géographie humaine" he puts the totality of what is social and of the environment of the *various countries* in their differences in the foreground. At the same time he points out the great importance of the spatial interconnection of the different parts of the earth surface within the whole of this surface (unité terrestre) [16].

That the principle of spatial differentiation found in the works of Brunhes and Vidal de la Blache also struck the attention of Cools, appears from the latter's definition of social geography as the concrete science of the regionally (i.e. spatially or chorologically) different ways of living of human groups on the surface of the earth [17].

The spatial differentiation of the modern world is extremely complicated. This also holds for the phenomena investigated and determined by social geography according to the Utrecht School way of positing problems. For under the influence of the striving after prosperity, and owing to the process of production the spatial human group will be differentiated into different social groups within the same living space. Their ways of life are no longer simple, but complicated. In a particular living space there is no longer one group, but there live different social groups, each of them in its own way involved in the life of the whole spatial human group of a living space. Economic-geographically speaking, there exists only one way of life in an agrarian region, viz., the agrarian form of living. Farmers and farm hands are both agrarians. In a socio-geographical sense, taking the concept social in a narrow sense, there are two different important social groups in this agrarian living space, viz., farmers and farm hands, if for a moment we ignore some other less important groups. In this short introduction we shall not enter any further into the problems that present themselves in this case with respect to spatial differentiation. They are, nevertheless, very complicated, if we think of the differences between agrarian and industrial regions. In agrarian regions there is usually no question of the different social groups living apart from each other in separate different parts of the living space, but in industrial regions there is.

By means of this all too short exposition of the interpretation of Brunhes and Vidal de la Blache's principles we only wish to establish that, however different the theoretical views of the nature of the phenomena examined by human geography may be, the principle of chorological or spatial differentiation remains intact.

We would submit as our personal conviction that spatial differentiation is the primary principle of all geographical sciences. Owing to this principle all the various kinds of geography, viz., social, political, economic geography, plant geography, physical, general, and special (regional) geography are geography.

This does not mean that there are no differences between these geographical sciences. If there were no differences, these different terms would be redundant. The geographical totality manifest in the interrelation of the spatial phenomena is different in each of the separate geographical sciences. But all the geographical sciences have for their object the chorological differentiation of a totality of terrestrial things and their phenomena. Their common aspect is constituted by their chorological differentiation.

By this we wish to point out that the concept geography in social and economic geography, in physical geography, and in general and special geography (regional geography), is not only maintained by the linguistic use of the *word* geography. We must oppose the view that the concept geography in each of these different geographic sciences has a really different content. In opposition to this view we agree with Hettner, who held that all geographical sciences have the same aspect, viz. the spatial or chorological aspect. In our opinion in this science the principle of chorological differentiation is the most fundamental concept.

In this study we shall try to give a more detailed analysis of the chorological differentiation of earthly reality, and to form a synthesis out of such an analysis, and to try to understand the meaning of the principle of chorological differentiation as an aspect of earthly reality.

CHAPTER II

CHOROLOGICAL DIFFERENTIATION AND REGION

Geography is usually defined as the study of the earth surface in its spatial diversity. The concepts earth surface and spatial are not entirely unobjectionable. The word earth surface refers to the ground, and even when we use it in a wider sense, it remains restricted to material things, whereas geography is interested both in material and immaterial things found on the surface of the earth. It may therefore be advisable to use the term world instead of the expression earth surface. The term world applies especially to the earth inclusive of what is found on it (in a material and an immaterial sense) [1].

As to the word "spatial", it connotes the dimensions of things. The concept chorological also implies the idea of spatial dimensions, but has some other connotations as well. Let us first examine the word spatial. By sensory space we refer to the three dimensions of a material object. Geography is the study of material and immaterial things, and for a moment we ignore the difficulty about what is meant by the dimensions of immaterial things. The material things investigated by geography have three dimensions, but geography lays the stress on the two dimensions that determine the surface. Geography is particularly concerned with surface extension. This surface extension is clearly expressed by the notion chorological, which has about the same content as the concepts areal and regional. In the concept space there is no special emphasis on the two surface dimensions. The three dimensions of sensory space are of equal value in this concept. Instead of the earth surface in its spatial diversity we prefer to speak of the world in its chorological diversity. Owing to this chorological diversity or differentiation of the world there are chorai, areas, regions, i.e., portions or parts of the world. These terms lay the stress on surface extension. Also when we speak of the contents of a region, we think of all that has surface extension. When in a description of the Po valley more attention is paid to the production of maize than to that of rice, this is due to the fact that the quantity of maize produced there is

10

much larger than that of rice. This may be so, but a geographer immediately thinks of the extent of the cultivated surface area which is many times larger in the case of the former crop than in that of the latter. So when we say that in geography the third dimension of things recedes a little into the background, it does not mean that this dimension in itself is of little importance. Nor is it indirectly unimportant in geography. In this science all three dimensions of a coal seam, e.g., are important. So are the height and relief of a mountain range. If there is a great deal of overground building in a town, the third dimension and the frequency of this overground building are very important, and are not ignored by geography. But in geography we first of all think of the surface extension of an area or of a region. This is not only the case when an area is flat, it also applies to a mountainous region, to a coal region, and to a town region, or to an urban district. Determinations within the third dimension are as it were further characteristics of the surface area.

Many German and Swiss geographers use the concept landscape, and though Hettner [2], Carol [3], Schmitthüsen and Bobek [4], and others include man and his works in it, this notion has occasioned a great deal of confusion, because it expresses only the material aspect of a portion of the world and the material things it contains. Carol is aware of this, but wants to maintain the idea and define it more accurately by means of the concept "Geomer". But in his explanation accompanied by the drawing of a cross section, the third dimension is of equal value with the two others which determine the surface extension. We will once more lay emphasis on the serious objections to such a view from a geographical standpoint. In geography the two dimensions of the horizontal surface are especially thought of, as appears from the notions geographic longitude and geographic latitude. Every spot on earth can be defined with the aid of its longitude and its latitude as well as with the aid of its altitude. This also holds for an area or a region when we define values within two limits or in averages. Only the determinations within the two dimensions of the horizontal surface, viz., longitude and latitude, are further defined as geographic longitude and geographic latitude. In the case of altitude, which is

11

a further determination within the third dimension, the indication geographic is lacking. This is why we give preference to the concepts chora, country, land, area and region, which terms emphasize the two horizontal dimensions and indications within the three dimensions. The distinction that will perhaps be necessary between the terms region and area we shall consider presently.

In addition to the word landscape many German geographers speak of earth space (Erdraum). Geography is the study of "the filled terrestrial spaces of the earth surface (der irdisch erfüllte Räume der Erdoberfläche)" [5]. Terrestrial should not be mistaken for the concept material. Ritter speaks of terrestrial, and this embraces material and immaterial things, and in this sense he has always interpreted the term. The meaning of the definition of geography quoted just now is clear. An earth space is not empty but contains objects. If for a moment we ignore our own objections against the use of the concept space with its three equivalent dimensions in geography, it is doubtful whether Ritter's expression is formally correct. For if it is, there must be an earth space outside of terrestrial objects. If a space is conceived of as an "ens rationis", and the reality of spatial dimensions is admitted, but not as realities in themselves, only as abstractions of the dimensions that objects have [6], the question suggesting itself is: Where is then the earth space, if these objects are thought away?

This point leads us to the problem of the way in which a chora, a region, or an area is determined by the spatial extension of the things in it, while as has been observed before, surface extension is most important to geography.

When we think of a portion of the world, and consequently of all these things in their spatial extension, so of the whole spatial complex, we think of something quite different from the idea, e.g. of the soil alone, or of a climate separately. In the first case we are thinking of a reality. And although in the second case it is difficult to deny that the soil and a particular condition of the atmosphere are realities, they are things and phenomena that have partly been abstracted from reality. Such a complex is a reality in which these things do not exist apart from each other and separately. If we consider the soil, vegetation, the atmosphere and its condition, man as a biological, economic, social and spiritual being separately, we are considering parts of reality. Man as a biological being and man as a cultural creature are not separated in reality, and man apart from the ground does not exist in reality either.

As we have already observed, the conception of an earth space (Erdraum) usually connotes a space filled with earthly things. It should, however, immediately be stated that this conception does not refer to a complex of things which is apart from, and independent of the space in which the complex of things is to be found. On the contrary, space and the things found in it are interconnected, but space in a geometrical sense is emphasized in this combination. The conception of an area is pretty well identical with that of an earth space. But the two dimensions of space forming the horizontal extension come more strongly to the fore in the concept area [7].

Our conception of an earth space is different. We put the matter the other way round. There does not exist a space containing earthly things, but there is only an earthly complex of material and immaterial things which is further determined by its absolute and its relative location on the terrestrial globe. Immaterial earthly things are connected with material things. Material things have dimensions, which are spatial characteristics, spatial properties. The dimensions of earthly things, and especially the two dimensions forming the horizontal extension of things, determine an earth space, an area. So our conception is concerned with the horizontal extension of the complex of things. In connection with this conception we will give a definite content in our study to various geographical concepts of space. In other words: We shall formulate our geographical spatial concepts and give them appropriate and customary names.

When the point at issue is the horizontal extension (chorological extension) of the whole complex of material and immaterial things somewhere on the globe, which complex has not yet been further analysed, and the question of its unity has not yet been raised, we speak of an *area*; the stress falls on the extension of the complex. We sometimes speak of a *land* and a *country* (this word taken in the sense of the German word Landstrich, Gegend), if in the earth

13

space the complex of things itself is stressed. But then, too, we often prefer the term area.

When, however, the discussion is concerned with the chorological extension of one object, or with that of a few (material and immaterial) things in such a complex displaying a certain amount of similarity in their characteristics, so that this portion of the world has a certain amount of similarity in accordance with these characteristics, we shall use the term *region* in this study. There is a certain unity in which the uniform chorological extension of the characteristics of one thing, or that of the characteristics of some different things is put in the foreground, e.g., a soil region, an economic region, and a climatic vegetation region.

We may speak of a *geographical region*, if also the uniform chorological extension of the "interrelation" of the characteristics of a thing with the characteristics of some other things comes to the fore.

The concept *chora* is more general and more indefinite in this study. It embraces all the other concepts of earth spaces. It only refers to a portion of the world which can be distinguished from the surrounding world, but for which any further definition by area, region and other concepts is not immediately necessary. Here, too, its horizontal extension is emphasized. It is clear that our concepts area, region, country, etc., do not refer to distinctions in the size of the surface.

The meaning of the concept region in economic region, soil region, vegetation region, etc., is always the same, but there is a marked difference in the nature of the surface extension, just as there is a distinction to be made between the regions of material and those of immaterial things.

The surface of the ground is uninterrupted, absolute, and so is that of the atmosphere. The vegetation surface is sometimes interrupted frequently, at other times rarely. The surface occupied by buildings and cultural works is mostly interrupted considerably.

To posit the problem of an area with its regions clearly we should first of all remember that there can be no question of an area unless it can be distinguished from other contiguous areas, and unless the various regions of an area are distinct from the regions of other

14

areas. If this was not the case, there would be only one area, one uniform earth surface, including one soil region, one climatic region, one vegetation region, one economic region, etc. In reality, however, there are a great variety of areas and great differentiation between the regions of the various areas.

To form a clear idea of an area and its different regions we shall construct in thought an area which is clearly distinct from its surrounding areas in every respect, and is to be sharply delimited from other areas. It goes without saying that such an area can hardly exist in reality. For although in reality there is an evident chorological differentiation of the world, the differentiations of things gradually pass over into each other, they cross and overlap each other very often. Every part that we isolate from the world as an area is never one perfect chorological differentiant, because the world is a whole, a continuum [8].

Our imaginary area has a sea clay soil, its atmospheric condition, its climate, has particular properties of temperature and moisture. Its vegetation is grass, its houses and farm-houses have a definite structure and function. Its economic life is based on dairy farming and on the breeding of pasture cattle. Its technique and its culture possess typical characteristics, and its inhabitants speak a linguistic dialect of their own. All these characteristics of the various phenomena are distinct from those in the surrounding areas.

The different regions that are to be distinguished on the ground of the characteristics of the various phenomena of this area display essential differences in the extension of their surface. The surface of the soil region is continuous and absolute, and so is the climate. The pasture vegetation forms a region interrupted by ditches, canals, roads, buildings, and by other territories. The type of buildings and farms constitutes a region which is very much interrupted. In comparison with the surface extension of the soil region the surface contents of the buildings resemble those of dots in a plane. Economic life is manifest in the labour, the aims, and the attitude to life of the inhabitants, which can also be partly observed in the cultivation of the soil, in its pasture vegetation, its cattle, its farms and dairy factories. So an economic region is a very strong abstraction as a region indeed. It is a portion of reality that can only be

15

determined by reflection and investigation. Its surface extension is determined by the living region of the inhabitants who have settled in this area, and who stamp it as an economic region on account of their work in connection with the various things we have mentioned. The surface extension of the various factors determining economic life, is for a large part strongly discontinuous, and also partly uninterrupted and absolute like the soil. The chorological extension of the linguistic region is determined by the living region of its inhabitants who speak its language. The residential, the economic and the linguistic region are not only concerned with material things, but also with immaterial phenomena.

Although all the regions of this area differ widely in surface extension, they are all of them representative of the area, even though their real surface extension is only small in comparison with the total surface of the area. The surface occupied by the buildings of a particular type is small compared with the surface extension of the ground. Yet we can say that this area forms a region with a particular type of dwelling house obtaining in the entire area, and characterizing it as a definite residential region.

This is an important point. When in a study on the Po valley a great deal of attention is given to the rice fields there, we can only say that they are a particularity of the Po valley in the sense that this valley has rice fields in contradistinction to many other areas in Europe which do not, or hardly cultivate this agricultural crop. These rice fields are only a small part of the Po valley in contrast with maize, wheat, and other cultures. The chorological extension, the chorological frequency of rice fields is only small in proportion to the whole of the surface extension of all the fields with crops in the Po valley.

In the case mentioned before, viz., of the houses of a fixed type, these dwelling houses are found in all parts of the area. Although in comparison with the total extent of that area its dwelling-houses occupy only a small part of it, we can nevertheless say that all the houses in that area have similar characteristics and that the region of this type of dwelling houses has the same chorological extension as the area. The region of this special type of houses is representative of this area. In its chorological extension the region

16

of the rice fields, however, is not representative of the Po valley. These fields may not be a curiosity of the Po valley, for this region is too large for it, but they are a peculiarity of such limited frequency that it is not characteristic of the Po valley as a whole. As a chorological differentiant the Po valley is insufficiently determined by the rice fields.

Although we must take exception to the term terrestrially filled space (irdisch erfüllte Raum), as has been indicated before, in connection with our further elucidation of the chorological extension of things, we once more wish to discuss an area in this sense.

When an area is more closely considered as an earth space, the ground and the atmosphere are the material things determining this terrestrial space. The other objects are found in this space. If we remember that surface extension is the essential characteristic of an area, the ground in its absolute chorological extension is obviously the most important component of an area. It is so not merely on account of this fact, for all the other things of an area cannot exist without the ground, but the ground could exist without the other things. This is not saying, of course, that the ground (i.e. the firm earth surface) can exist without the interior of the earth. But this interior does not belong to the surface of the earth (or world) and is not the object of geography. The statement that the ground is the most important component of an area does not imply that without the other things the ground would be what it is now owing to the influence of the atmosphere, the water, organic and human life. But within the complex of the things of an area the ground is conceivable without the other things. The atmosphere rests on the ground, the latter is the prerequisite of the former and not vice versa. Vegetation is found on the ground, man rests, stands, and moves about on the ground. The idea of an area in the first place suggests the ground, the material thing on which the other things are located. The notions of a dwelling-place and of a living space primarily refer to the ground, the firm earth surface. Although the ground is the first thing and the pre-requisite of all the others, it is not the only pre-requisite. The other things also pre-suppose one another. There is no possibility of natural life without the atmosphere, and vegetation cannot subsist on the

17

soil only, the warmth and moisture of the atmosphere are equally indispensable.

Considering the chorological extension of earthly things we speak of vegetation regions, living regions, economic regions, etc. All these regions are absolutely dependent on the chorological extension of the ground. The living-region is determined by the extension of the ground with its more or less densely spread population and its houses scattered here and there in larger or smaller numbers. With the exception of the atmosphere, which has an absolute spatial extension, all other earthly things are more or less densely distributed over the surface of the ground. So when we speak of the chorological extension of vegetation, of an economical form of production, and of a particular type of houses, of a vegetation region, an economic region, a region of a particular type of dwelling houses, the extension and the form of these regions are determined by the region of the ground on which the other things are spread in a particular degree of density.

Although it is difficult to distinghuish the non-human from what is human, or nature from culture [9], because in reality, they are interwoven and interlaced, this distinction is unavoidable, though with some restrictions, if we wish to define the various factors with which geography is concerned.

Nature, and especially the ground, is a pre-requisite of human existence and culture. But we cannot say that the chorological differentiation of nature and the ground is a determining factor of the chorological diversity of human life and culture. The ground and other physical and biotic things offer particular possibilities within certain limits. These possibilities are also connected with human culture. Individual and collective human action together with the possibilities found in nature and in the ground constitute human subsistence and culture. Without nature and the ground any human existence is impossible. Even in the case e.g. of the importation of raw materials and auxiliary materials, capital goods and consumers' goods from other areas, production and subsistence in a particular area are only possible with the aid and on the ground of this area as an establishing, living and traffic region. It is impossible to establish any natural existence in a vacuum. Nature,

18

the ground, is determining in a negative sense. If there is no nature, no ground, the inevitable consequence is that there is no subsistence. In a positive sense nature and the ground are pre-requisites and conditions of human existence, and after them particular possibilities of human existence can be considered.

When we speak of the different possibilities of nature and the soil, we certainly do not mean to say that a geographer should try to find these different possibilities. When he studies a particular area, he has to deal with a particular soil, which is used in a particular way. A geographer studies reality. If this soil should offer different possibilities, he is only concerned with the possibility that has been used and is actual reality now. But if we still keep speaking of various possibilities, we wish to indicate that the way of life realized is not exclusively determined by this particular kind of soil.

Let us consider the case of an area with a young sea clay soil. One half of it is used as arable land, and in the other half the means of subsistence is dairy farming and pasture cattle-breeding. If this area is considered from an economic standpoint, it is a clear case of chorological differentiation: an arable region and a dairy farming and cattle-breeding region. In both economic regions the two possibilities offered by the sea clay soil are indispensable pre-requisites. But the decision as to which of them shall be used in each of them is not determined by the soil and other factors, but finally by man.

Among their various possibilities, different kinds of soil may have one in common that has been used in actual reality. In this connection we are referring to such a case as that of sea clay and peat-bog, which are both destined for dairy farming and cattle-breeding. The differentiation of the soil, the difference between the two soils, is not the decisive factor here. There is no differentiation of the way of life and the form of production. The inhabitants have chosen the same form of production.

To determine the importance of the soil for the chorological differentiation of the way of life it is necessary to make use of comparison. On the one hand areas with different soils and with different kinds of production must be compared with areas that have different soils but are used in the same way. On the other hand areas with similar soils and similar production should be compared with areas of the same kind of soil and different kinds of production.

As a matter of fact a geographer who studies a particular area can never restrict himself to that one area. To ascertain and define an area or a region some knowledge of other areas and regions is required from which this one is to be distinguished either by means of a difference in soil, in vegetation or in crop, in form of production, or in some other element of the earthly complex. Precisely on the difference from other chorai the peculiarity of a chora is based. On this difference we also base the designation of a chora. Its description starts from these differences, and to ascertain the significance of a differentiant it is necessary to compare it with other chorai, above all with contiguous ones. We shall revert to this problem, which occurs here only as a side-issue, in Chapter VII, where it will be discussed in greater detail.

What we have explained with respect to the significance of the soil for the chorological differentiation of the way of life, is in a certain sense also applicable to the climate. The same climate often has various possibilities of growing different cultivated crops, and within their possibilities different climates often share the same possibility for the cultivation of one and the same crop.

This is due to the action of man, who makes a choice in connection with his way of life. Also in the relation of the chorological differentiations of the elements in nature we notice the divergence of the differentiations. Areas with the same kind of soils may have different climates. This also holds for soils and vegetation. Areas with different soils often have similar climates, and vegetation does not always run parallel with the differentiation of climate.

The soil itself has often changed a great deal. Soils that were originally different, and whose sub-soils are still different, generally show great similarity in the upper soil on account of the same process of weathering caused by the similarity in climate. Man, too, works the ground, makes similar soils different, and dissimilar soils equivalent to a high degree.

20

Let us revert to the problem for the sake of which we have after all brought forward all that has preceded. This problem is concerned with the diversity of areas and within the latter with the diversity of regions, i.e., the chorological differentiation of terrestrial things and phenomena. Are we to infer from what has been said above that the diversity of nature, and in particular that of the soil, is not so very important for the diversity of the way of life and that of civilization? Such a conclusion would be an error. If there were no differentiation of nature and of the soil, the diversity of the way of life and of civilization would be many times smaller than it is. And if the ground were the same everywhere on earth, the differentiation of climate as well as that of vegetation would be much smaller, although the diversity of vegetation shows a more intensive interrelationship with the differentiation of climate. The significance of the diversity of the ground for the differentiation of the way of life, the climate and vegetation should not be underestimated. Especially the forms of the earth, such as highland, hillside or mountain slope, lowland, mountains, a smooth or an uneven territory, are very important for the differentiation of the way of life, the climate, the water condition, vegetation, and for other physical and biotic phenomena.

From the above, however, the conclusion is inevitable that on the whole the ground (soil) may be the most fundamental and the formative element of an area, but the chorological differentiation of the ground is not the only or the determining factor of the differentiation of all the other things of an area. The ground is the indispensable factor to human life and culture, to the waters and the climate, to vegetation and to the fauna in general, but the chorological differentiation of the ground is not the decisive factor of the chorological differentiation of the other earthly things. This latter fact is very significant for geography. Geography is not concerned with the general characteristics that areas and things in them have in common, not with what is of the greatest general importance in them. Neither the ground in general, nor human existence in general, are the objects of geographical study. No more is the latter concerned with the interrelated complex of things constituting an area in general. The object of geography is the chorological

21

differentiation of the interrelated complex of earthly things constituting the areas in their diversity [10].

In so far as this is possible, the investigation of the diversity of these areas will have to establish which of the chorologically differentiating things are of greater importance or less important for the chorological differentiation of other things in these areas.

As to the soil, however, there is another factor which brings out the importance of the soil for the chorological differentiation. As we have already observed, this is the fact that the same kind of soil in different areas possesses a diversity of vegetation or cultivated crops, of economic and cultural life. This is the significance of the different possibilities that one and the same kind of soil has for the chorological differentiation of other earthly things. It is true, this significance should not be overestimated. Its possibilities are often restricted. On peat the growth of a good wheat crop is pretty well impossible. From an economic point of view, when the costs are considered, not all the possibilities presenting themselves in a technical sense can be realized. Earthly reality clearly shows us that only few of these possibilities have been actualized.

When in the conclusion of an important treatise on geography Polspoel [11] emphasizes the differentiation of the earth surface and opposes the latter to man, he means above all the solid surface of the earth, i.e. the ground. In this connection we would like to explain the significance of the ground for geography once again. There is no chorological differentiation of other terrestrial things possible without the ground. The ground is the indispensable prerequisite of the existence of all forms of chorological differentiation. The chorological extension of the regions formed by the chorological differentiation of the other earthly objects is dependent on the absolute chorological extension of the ground on which these objects are spread more or less densely. This dependence of the regions of the other earthly objects on the ground is something different from the problem of the degree to which the regions formed by the chorological differentiation of the ground determine the regions that can be distinguished on the basis of the chorological differentiation of the other objects. In connection with the above we can say the following about the significance of the chorological differentiation of the ground as a determining factor for the chorological differentiation of the other terrestrial things:

1. The chorological differentiation of the ground is partly of immediate significance for the chorological differentiation of other earthly things.

2. Owing to their possessing different possibilities, similar soils in various areas have realized chorological differentiations of other things, such as vegetation, cultivated crops, economic and cultural life.

Man in particular is the determining factor of the significance of the ground in its chorological differentiation. The diversity of the soil of the different areas has been partly utilized by man in the diversity of vegetation, economic life, and culture. But man has also answered the chorological differentiation of the soil with the same vegetation and the same kind of economic life and culture owing to the presence of a common possibility of the different kinds of soil. In addition, man has converted the different possibilities of similar soils of various areas into a chorological differentiation of cultivated crops, of economic and cultural life.

The importance of the ground in geography cannot be easily overestimated. We agree with Polspoel's dictum that geography without "gē" (in this case especially the solid earth surface, i.e., the ground) is unthinkable. But the significance of the ground (soil) in geography is something very complicated. We will explain this once again with the aid of the concepts area and region.

Let us think of two adjoining areas, one with a sea clay soil, the other with low peat. Both areas have grass vegetation with dairy farming and pasture cattle-breeding industries. The form and the size of these industries, cow-houses and barns, show a high degree of similarity. The drainage of the land of both has been co-ordinated. Are there two separate areas? We have mentioned two adjoining areas, and so we have thought of the difference between these two. Apparently we have been led by the fact that there is a difference in soil, viz. clay and low peat. If we consider the way of life, however, there is no difference, no chorological differentiation. We can establish that there are two soil regions, but there is

23

one economic region. This also holds for vegetation, for there is only one vegetation region.

The reverse also occurs: an area with a sea clay soil one part of which is used for cattle-breeding and dairy farming, and the other adjoining part is destined to serve as arable land with sugar beets. Economic life, the ways of life in the two parts are widely different. There are two economic regions, but there is one soil region, and as to vegetation (cultivated crops), there are two vegetation regions. But again the question arises: Is there only one, or are there two areas?

In both these cases we can establish that the presence or absence of a differentiated soil is not decisive of the diversity or the similarity of vegetation and the way of life. The differentiation and the similarity of the latter two things are closely connected with the dissimilarity and the similarity of human action utilizing particular possibilities of different and of similar soils.

This is decisive of the ascertainment of the vegetation regions and the economic regions mentioned in connection with the soil. As to the areas, we must remember that by this word we have referred to the reality of the entire chorological complex of things. Although in a region we consider part of this reality separately, these things do not exist separately and apart from each other. In an area we comprise all material and immaterial things, the whole of reality.

When, however, we call a portion of terrestrial world a separate area, because the soil of this area consists of sea clay, in contradistinction to an adjoining part of the world which we call another area, because there the soil is low peat, we have already expressed a view, a judgment about the full (entire) reality, namely an opinion on the chorological reality and on the chorological differentiation with respect to the soil. It would be the same thing, if we should speak of one separate area in that part of the world because there is one particular way of life, and of two areas because there are two different ways of life in those portions of the world. Then we have expressed an opinion on the chorological reality, and on the chorological differentiation of that reality with reference to the way of life. The same applies to vegetation (cultivated crops).

24

A part of the world is a chorological complex of things with a very complicated structure, and probably with even more complicated relationships of a causal, functional and final nature, since it is a complex of physical and biotic objects, and of things of the mind [12]. It is a chorological totality that has all kinds of facets.

We have already mentioned the chorological differentiation into regions when the chorological differentiation of the separate objects of the world is the centre of interest. This view led to the distinction between soil regions, climatic regions, vegetation regions, economic regions. But in this conception we have already pointed out the more or less close mutual relations of these regions. The chorological differentiations of vegetation and of climate are closely connected, the chorological differentiation of the way of life resulting in the diversity of economic regions is more or less strongly interwoven with the chorological differentiations of the soil, the climate, vegetation, and the things of material and spiritual culture. So we must try to analyse the chorological differentiation of the whole complex of things, the total reality of the areas in the chorological differentiation of a limited number of different complexes of a less complicated nature with a strong integration. This is one way; the other way is the attempt to connect the chorological differentiations of the separate things that have resulted in soil regions, vegetation regions, climatic regions, economic regions and others in proportion to the greater or lesser significance that the chorological differentiations of these separate things have for each other. This means that from soil regions we should proceed to pedological-geographic regions, from climatic to climatological-geographic regions, and from economic to economic-geographic regions. Geography is concerned with the chorological differentiation of the complex of earthly things, with the totality. To gain an insight into this total chorological differentiation it is necessary to analyse the interrelated complex of things contained in the reality of the areas into separate elements, and to reconstruct the latter synthetically so as to form different unities of totality.

CHAPTER III

ANALYSIS OF THE VERTICAL CHOROLOGICAL COMPLEX

In the previous chapter we imagined, — among other things for the exposition of the essential differences in the surface extension of the various terrestrial things —, an area which was clearly distinguishable in every respect from the surrounding areas (cf. pp. 15 and ff.). This construction was legitimate, because the specific problem that was to be elucidated was not changed by this procedure. The problem could be made clearer with the aid of that imaginary area. But it must be emphatically stated that in reality areas cannot be distinguished from each other in every respect (i.e., in all those material and immaterial things). The chorological differentiations of the things of the world for a great part do not coalesce but overlap, and the differentiations of separate things gradually merge into one another and can hardly ever be sharply delimited from each other. It is true, there are areas, such as small islands, which approach to a total chorological differentiant, and there are differentiations that are indeed distinguishable from each other without any transition, such as the differentiation of the world according to the states. As a rule a state has a surface extension that is accurately defined; the chorological differentiation of the political status forms regions that display the most sharply defined boundaries.

On the whole, however, we may say, that the world is a continuum, and in whatever way its areas are delimited, they are never perfect total chorological differentiants. The reason, however, is not only that the differentiations of the separate things do not always have the same surface extension, for there is another reason as well why the world is a continuum and the areas are not self-supporting and independent. Owing to their relative location and the processes of motion there are horizontal relations between the things and their phenomena in the different places of the world, both those that are close together and those that are farther away from each other. An area no more than the smallest portion of the

26

world has an isolated existence [1]. An area is never an independent whole. Only the earth surface, the world, as a whole, has an existence as a unity.

Hettner says: "The earth, however, is not something simple, but perhaps the most complicated structure we know. It is almost as if various architects with various ideas have worked at it, so that the internal arrangement does not correspond with the plan but originates from other considerations, and it also looks as if the two architects have changed their minds more than once during the process of building. The earth surface owes its constitution to a plurality of causes that have nothing to do with each other" [2]. After man has changed the earth surface into a world by means of his activities in the spheres of economics, politics, and culture, the structure becomes even more complicated. It is Hartshorne [3] especially who has analysed this complexity of the world, and has shown that it is impossible to determine areas that display a unity of total chorological differentiation.

When in accordance with the indications at the end of the previous chapter we want to analyse the chorological differentiation of the complex of things, we should bear in mind that no chorologically differentiated complex is self-contained and independent, i.e., every place and area is related to other places and areas.

On a closer examination of chorologically differentiated complexes of things two kinds of chorological integration can be distinguished:

1. The integration of things and their phenomena at any point of the earth surface, which we call *vertical interrelation*.

2. The relations between things and their phenomena at different points or places in the world on the ground of their relative location, which we will call *horizontal interconnection* [4].

These two kinds of integration are decisive, but it is clear that the chorological differentiation is directly related with the vertical interrelation, and only indirectly with the horizontal interconnection. For chorological differentiation means that the things of one place are different from those in other localities. At every point of the earth differentiated things influence one another, and are

27

integrated into a vertical interrelationship. The horizontal relations exert a great influence on it, but they do not immediately manifest themselves in our experience, when we observe the chorological diversity. The weather in our country is strongly dependent on the atmospheric conditions and the atmospheric movement above the Atlantic Ocean and various parts of the continent of Europe. In other areas the soil is also determined by the soil dust carried there by the winds from other areas. Rivers, glaciers, and seas carry silt and debris from one place to another. People deliberately carry goods and raw materials by sea and land, and through the air, from one place to another. But we know the results of these horizontal interconnections first, and next the movement that has brought them about. On a certain spot there arise vertical inter-relations of autochtonic and imported, exotic things.

Horizontal interconnections are also differentiated over the earth surface. These interconnections are widely different in character and degree. This depends on the nature of the phenomena in the various localities between which the horizontal interconnections are found, and on the distance between such localities. In order to distinguish geographic regions from each other and to determine these regions on the basis of the chorological differentiation of the horizontal interconnections, — each of these regions possessing a certain degree of unity concerning the horizontal interconnection between the localities in this region, — it is necessary to analyse these horizontal interconnections according to their degree of integration and in connection with the distance between the localities in question. Such an examination is only possible after the vertical local inter-relations have been established which are the source from which the horizontal interconnections arise.

For this reason, and because the chorological differentiation can be observed immediately only in the local vertical interrelations both of autochthonic and imported, exotic things, we will begin with the vertical interrelations and examine the horizontal inter-connections later on.

The word vertical interrelation suggests the third dimension. In the previous chapter we have pointed out that this dimension recedes a little into the background in geography, and that is why it is necessary again to give a short explanation of this concept of vertical interrelationship. By this integration we mean the interrelation of the chorological differentiations that are found in the same locality. Strictly speaking, this is an impossibility. The space occupied by one thing cannot be the space of other things at the same time. We might say: Many things are found one above the other on the same surface. The atmosphere rests on the ground; vegetation, houses and inhabitants are also found on the ground. But the atmosphere, the water and the roots of the plants are found in the ground as well. The third dimension, which in the geographic view is, as it were, a characteristic of the other two dimensions, the upper surface, enables us to speak of things that are found in the same place. The vertical interrelation, therefore, means the integration of the differentiated things and phenomena that are situated in each other and interlaced with each other in a small earth space. In a vertical integration in which human phenomena are involved, the vertical interrelation can be given a wider meaning. In a village there are a few shops and schools, a church, a cultural centre, etc. These things are at the disposal of the inhabitants of the village, and are integrated into the lives of the village people in various degrees of closeness. In this case, too, we would speak of vertical interrelations, as in thought we identify the separate localities of the shops, the schools, the church and the cultural establishments with the place of the houses of the inhabitants in the village. We should be careful, however. In reality there are here also horizontal interconnections, which, however, we ignore. In how far culture and technique play a part in the conquest of distances, and thus reduce the horizontal interconnections, is another story, which will be discussed in a later context. It must be said, however, that in many cases vertical and horizontal integrations are merged.

In a wider sense a vertical interrelation may be circumscribed as the integration of the differentiations of things and phenomena in the same place.

The complex of the vertical interrelations consists of organic and anorganic things, and those of the mind. Material things have magnitude, form, material conditions and structure. These things are connected with each other by all kinds of relations, and they have a function in each other's existence. The immaterial things have an internal structure and function in each other's existence, and are connected with the material anorganic and organic things by their functional relationships. We emphatically point out that vertical interrelationship is especially of a functional nature. Things influence each other locally.

Bobek and Schmithüsen speak of a structure of action (Wirkungsgefüge) of the anorganic and organic world and the world of the mind. "In the functional spheres and structures of these three realms there obtain various kinds of law-conformities (Gesetzmässigkeiten), viz. 1. physical causality; 2. vital law-conformity, of which up to now it has not been possible to decide whether in the last resort it can be reduced to physical causality; 3. the autonomous law-conformity (Eigengesetzlichkeit), characteristic of a spiritually determined being, especially in its social interconnectedness" [5]. It may be useful to define these law-conformities a little more accurately with the aid of von Handel's [6] view of the various forms of law-conformity. He mentions causal (deterministic and statically causal) laws and vital and final causal laws. The latter also operate in the anorganic world. And he speaks of causal laws in spiritual life which display a certain amount of analogy with the causal laws of material physical phenomena, but are not identical with them. The laws of spiritual life lack the characteristic of prediction, but they possess the peculiarity that the process of cause and effect can be established and indicated afterwards. It should be borne in mind that in many cases it is difficult to distinguish between cause and effect on account of interaction, and functional interdependence.

During the last few decades several German publications have appeared which bear on the structure and function of the complex of things that form a landscape. We have already quoted some passages from the work of Bobek and Schmithüsen. Also in another study by Schmithüsen [7] these problems are elaborately discussed. Among the other writings in this field we should make special mention of the works of Troll [8] and Paffen [9]. They concern the soil in its physico-chemical-biotic structure and function both as regards the vertical and the horizontal integration. The latter two authors speak of morphology and ecology in which the object of the inquiry is the structure and the function of the complex respectively. Paffen [10] elaborately and thoroughly deals with the structure of interaction (Wechselwirkungsgefüge) and with the dynamics of interactions (Wechselwirkungsdynamik) of the complex of physical, chemical and biotic factors which have a "totality" (ganzheitlich) character. In addition to the economics of nature (Naturhaushaltkunde) or the ecology of the physical-chemical-biotic complex there is also an economics of landscapes, when human activity and relationships with the environment are integrated into the structure of interaction of the cultivated landscape. To our mind Troll and Paffen are right when they say that the physical-chemical-biotic causalities that govern the natural structure of interaction (naturbürtige Wechselwirkungsgefüge) and belong to the ecology of a landscape, cannot be applied to the field of energy of a cultivated landscape, if the centre of interest is the purposeful action of man and human relations to his natural environment. According to these two authors ecology and economics are together able to analyse the structure and the function of a landscape and those of man's cultivated landscape.

However important the ideas of these writers may be, as well as their further elaboration, we shall go further into the matter in a later context, it should be remembered, however, that geography is concerned with the chorological differentiation of structure and function, with the chorological diversity of the structure of interaction, and not with the interaction within this complex in general.

Geography, therefore, deals with the chorological differentiation of the totality of things and their phenomena, and of their interrelationships. The important point is the fact that the particular chorological differentiations of one thing and its phenomena do not have the same significance for the particular chorological differentiations of other things and phenomena. The particular chorological variations of the atmospheric condition as regards temperature and moisture do not have the same significance for the chorological

31

differentiation of natural vegetation and cultivated crops. The differentiation of temperature is more important for the differentiation of cultivated crops, except in hot and dry regions, where the variation of insufficient moisture is more important. The differentiation of moisture is more significant for the differentiation of natural vegetation, except in sub-polar and polar regions, where the variation of insufficient warmth is more important. For the differentiation of the soils the significance of the variation in temperature and moisture is again different, although there is a certain analogy with the relation between the climatic elements and natural vegetation. If we pay attention to the importance of the chorological variation of temperature and moisture for the chorological variation of the labour produced by the people, the quantitative values of temperature and moisture and the interrelation of the two climatic elements are again different, in which case there is also a great difference between the variations of bodily or of mental labour [11].

In many respects the same thing holds for the ground. Not only the profile of the ground, but also the form of the surface is important, such as smoothness or unevenness, and the inclination of a territory. Characteristics are said to be significant only from a particular viewpoint. Their significance is in the first place determined with special reference to agriculture. Agriculture is always benefited by the fertility of the soil, which in its turn is dependent on the physical qualities of texture and structure of the soil, of its chemical and organic composition, of the water supply condition, and the circulation of the air. They influence each other mutually. Extensive mechanical agriculture, however, is at least as much benefited by the evenness and smoothness of a territory as by its fertility, as it is a favourable condition for the use of agricultural machinery. These agricultural machines must be able to work a large field in a short time, and for this mobile agriculture the smoothness of the ground is very important. So in this case there is a close relation between the technical economic process and the form of the ground, but in dry areas such as the Great Plains the texture as well as the smoothness of the soil are essential. A soil of a fine texture will hold the water of the scarce rains better.

The large quantity of mechanical energy at the disposal of every farmer in the Great Plains enables him to work the upper soil continually in the form of raking and combing up to prevent the evaporation of the rising capillary water. In this mechanical procedure the smoothness of the soil is a great advantage, and all the more effective when the soil has a fine texture, which holds the water as much as possible. In other countries, such as certain areas in the old China with a very dense population and often with little modern technique, fertility is of the greatest importance. Every plot of ground must be worked intensively to make the yield as large as possible. Unevenness of the ground was hardly a disadvantage in this kind of agriculture, which up to very recent times was exclusively based on the use of human force (animate energy). The relief of the soil is even very important for the formation of a natural water-reservoir for irrigation purposes. The slopes facilitate the laying out of terraces, which are very important for a better irrigation. The latter is made possible by the abundant precipitation of the wet monsoon. In the former self-sufficient "hsien" there was no exchange of goods of any importance. The harvest was hardly sufficient to feed the dense population. There was no need of modern roads for the transport of goods and persons in this local economy. This means that the relief, which always entails its own difficulties for the transport of persons and goods, had no prejudicial influence here. In opposition to this the thinly populated agricultural regions of the Great Plains are even benefited by the evenness of the territory, as far as traffic is concerned. For these regions are dependent on the exchange of the wheat produced for capital goods and articles of consumption. Railways and motor roads are indispensable in this interlocal economy, and then, of course, an even territory is a natural advantage [12].

These examples may show how much the relations between the various things and phenomena may differ. Economic life in one area is bound up with one kind of natural things and phenomena, and in other areas with other things and phenomena. In the Great Plains an even and smooth soil of a fine texture, and a dry and rather hot climate, are important physical elements with respect to the economy of mobile extensive dry-farming with a strongly

33

interlocal traffic. In south-east China, on the other hand, the local economy of an intensive agriculture with animate energy is closely connected with the fertility of the soil, with relief and the hot wet monsoon climate.

As has been observed, the soil has physical, chemical, and biotic characteristics. The water supply position and the circulation of the air are in a certain sense separate conditions, but they are nevertheless connected with the characteristics mentioned. The various soils are distinguishable from each other by means of the differences in these qualities. The first three groups of characteristics, however, are not independent of each other, but influence each other mutually. The distinction and classification of soils lay special emphasis on their physical properties [13]. But the chemical properties influence the physical ones. Thus a particular percentage of chalk (lime) influences the structure of the crumbs. Clay, sand and peat are soils that are clearly distinguishable from each other. Each of them has a group of interrelated characteristics which form a whole, which wholes are mutually different. Clay, sand and peat are notions each of which means a separate unity, i.e., the characteristics of each of these concepts are no elements that exist at random and apart from each other [14]. On the other hand, however, clay, peat and sand do not differ from each other in every respect. They are no incompatible concepts. All three soils can be used for pasture vegetation, although the quality is not the same in all of them. But this difference in quality is a great deal smaller than the difference in the quality and the quantity of wheat, if such a crop should be grown on these soils.

On certain kinds of clay soil, pasture is possible as well as the growth of wheat. In the two cases, however, different qualities of the soil are utilized. In the one case particular characteristics are of primary importance, whereas the other qualities are secondary and even tertiary. In the other case the significance of the characteristics is different. When there is pasture cattle-breeding on clay, peat and sand, it is not the differences between these concepts of the soil that are put in the foreground, but the properties they have in common. Of course, certain corresponding characteristics are intensified by the activity of the farmers, whose use of the soil is

34

intended to reach the same end. But the soils remain clay, sand and peat, and differ if we pay attention to other characteristics. The latter enable us to distinguish these soils into clay, peat and sand. The presence of common characteristics is proved by the fact that in Central Europe these three soils are included in the group of the grey-brown forest soils (podzolic soils).

This means that although different soils are differentiated by groups of characteristics that form a whole on account of their interrelations, this whole is not a rigid combination. In connection with particular vegetations and crops used by man for his way of life the combination of characteristics proves to be dynamic. The combination possesses different possibilities within definite limits. The significance of the different characteristics varies in these combinations with the different crops that are cultivated.

If the different soils are considered in their interrelation with manufacturing industry, quite different characteristics will come to the fore to distinguish between them and to qualify them. Recall, e.g. the importance of the various soils, especially of the deeper layers of the ground, to mining, or that of the upper layers as raw material for a particular production, such as clay for brick making. For setting up an industry among other things, the firmness of the ground is very important. From an agrarian point of view the soft and low-lying clay and peat soils of the western part of the Netherlands may rank higher than the firm sandy soils of the south-east and the centre, but from the standpoint of those who want to establish an industry the latter soils have great advantages. The costs of building factories, houses and other edifices, and the costs of building roads and railways, and laying out territories, and keeping all these in good repair, are a great deal smaller on high firm sandy soils. On low-lying grounds ramming is necessary, often to great depths, and the level of the ground must be raised. The high water level occasions extra mill drainage. The laying out and the keeping up of underground works, especially those of sewage, are much more expensive in a low-lying marshy soil: There are great hydrological difficulties to be overcome. The supply of drinking water, too, in the low regions below sea level necessitates higher costs [15].

From the above it can be inferred that the characteristics of the chorological differentiations of physical objects, such as the atmosphere and the soil, have a different significance in connection with economic life, and that this significance depends on the nature of the economic phenomena. The economic phenomena may bear on agriculture or on industry, which can be divided into arable farming, horticulture, pasture cattle-breeding and dairy farming, sylviculture, on the one hand, and into light and heavy industries on the other. From another point of view industries may be divided into exporting industry and industry catering for the regional market, into basic and non basic industry and into agrarian industry and industry proper, and there are many other distinctions to be made for the agrarian and the industrial trades. All these different forms of economic life are interrelated with the soil, but in widely different ways. And further, the significance of the characteristics of physical things in their interrelation with the way of life varies with the differences of technique and the cultural level of the human groups in a particular area. The interrelation of physical and biotic things apart from human influence is a great deal less complicated. The laws obtaining in such an interrelation are simpler when compared with those governing human phenomena. The relations between physical and biotic things are of a more static nature, in contradistinction to those of the human phenomena and the relations of human and physical phenomena, which are dynamic.

Up till now we have chiefly discussed the complex of the interrelationships of physical and economic objects. The interrelation of political and purely cultural things with physical things is of an entirely different nature. High mountains on the frontier of a state form a serious obstacle to traffic, but may be of positive value as a protection from an aggressive neighbouring state in a politico-military interrelation, whereas in an economic interrelationship they may be of a negative significance. Certain characteristics of economic, political and social things are often very important for purely cultural phenomena and form a totality of interrelations, while the relations between such cultural phenomena with many physical and biotic phenomena can be traced only with difficulty. These relations are often mediated by the relations of the economic with the physical phenomena. Economic chorological differentiations may be very important for the discovery of cultural and socio-political chorological differentiations, because economic life exercises a great influence on the other factors of human life. In a different context, Hartshorne says: "For most of the people of the world, a major part of their activity is concerned with ways and means of keeping body and soul together, or more correctly, with making a living —, i.e. economic activities. Likewise the greater part of the land area of the world used by man is used for economic activities" [16]. This is especially clear in the agrarian sector. The interconnectedness with physical things is more marked here than in industry. In the industrial phenomena there is much more question of man subjecting and dominating nature, but in the agrarian phenomena the active adaptation to nature comes to the fore. The economic purpose here also directs the activities, but displays more interrelation and harmony with nature. Many cultural and social characteristics can only be understood in connection with the relations between the economic and physico-biotic phenomena. The central feature in this complicated whole is the farm as a unit. Hartshorne describes the interrelation of the economic with the physical and biotic phenomena at the farm as follows: "The farm, as an organized unit, includes not merely the land and the plants and buildings on it, but also the livestock, tools, methods and intensity of production, and the use of products. Each and all of the elements listed, whether material fields, buildings or tools, or immaterial methods of production, can be understood in form and function only in terms of the whole farm unit" [17]. For geography this means that very probably there is a close relationship between the chorological diversity of social and cultural phenomena in rural areas and the chorological differentiation of the complex of phenomena of the farm.

Generally speaking we can say that the chorological differentiation of the interrelation of human phenomena with the physical phenomena depends on the diversity of the cultural level in the different areas at a particular period of time.

In the above exposition we have got acquainted with many and

37

various interrelations within the vertical chorologically varying complex of things and phenomena. Thus we can state the following:

1. The vertically differentiated complex of phenomena in one locality can be analysed into various integrations in which often part of the same elements play a rôle, although these elements have a different significance in each of the different integrations (e.g. the interrelation of climate with mental labour on the one hand and with cultivated crops on the other).

2. Particular vertical interrelations of different localities display a certain relatedness, but the importance of the characteristics of the elements of which the interrelations have been composed is often very different (e.g. the interrelation of the soil and agriculture in one place, and the interrelation of the soil and manufacturing industry in another place).

Now the question arises whether the relation of particular vertical interrelations in different localities on earth is of such a nature that these interrelations can be considered to be of the same kind? And if so, is it on the whole possible to analyse the chorologically varying complex of phenomena according to fixed principles into integrations that differ mutually in an essential way, and can be distinghuished into different kinds of integrations that are at the same time important?

Let us first discuss the question about the importance of the integrations. We have elaborately explained that the chorological differentiations of the separate things and their phenomena are important or significant, if there is interrelationship between these chorological differentiations or variations. We are not concerned with the separate variations as such, but with the totality of the differentiations, as an area is a chorological totality or a chorological complex. The greater the influence is that a differentiation — a differentiated thing — has on another, or the more it is influenced by another, and the closer their interrelationship is, the greater will be the significance of the respective differentiations for this particular area. Also in the analysis of the complex into a number of separate interrelations of a less complicated character we were concerned with the mutual function and significance of the differentiations within a definite integration. The importance of a differentiation has, therefore, been determined by its significance for other differentiations in an area, assuming of course that the chorological extension of this differentiation is representative of such an area as a whole. Next we have given special attention to the ground in its significance for other terrestrial things. The ground, the soil is an important factor, independent of the question as to whether the variation or the absense of variation of the soil is decisive of the differentiation of the other terrestrial things.

However, the element "important" has also been unwittingly used in the sense of a qualification of something. We consider certain characteristics of the soil "important" to arable farming; other characteristics are important to pasture cattle-breeding; others again to the building of factories, etc. These characteristics are not only important because certain chorological differentiations of the soil based on these characteristics are interrelated with the chorological differentiations of economic life that have been mentioned, but because we consider economic life and its variations in agriculture, cattle-breeding and industry as important concerns. We thought this to be self-evident. But it implies more. Are economic life and its variations important to geography, and are *all* the chorological differentiations that are closely interrelated really important in a geographic respect?

Hartshorne says that in geography the phenomena of nature should be considered "with reference to man's point of view — nature as man is concerned with it" [18]. In his last work he enters more deeply into this problem, also under the influence of some ideas advanced by Cholley, Schmitthenner and Plewe. Hartshorne says: "The earth surface is in fact our universe, the world in which we live, and which we can directly experience. What to the astronomer is only the outer shell of one of the minor planets of one of the lesser stars in one of innumerable galaxies is to all mankind our world, and the only world we know. Geography is not, therefore, merely like all of science in being anthropocentric, because only man studies science. The subject of study in geography, the world — even in those parts of it in which there are no men, — is viewed as man's world" [19].

Schmitthenner says: "In geography, and even within the

39

natural sciences only in geography, man is the measure" [20].

Cholley declares: "The concept of geography finally proves to denote a kind of philosophy of man considered as the principal inhabitant of the planet" [21]. Hartshorne further defines this notion by adding: "The earth as the home of man . . . Home in the fullest sense as that part of the physical universe which constitutes the world we experience". The significance of the earth as the world of man has varied in the course of time, and is different to different people in the same period of time [22]. (On the anthropocentric character of geography Ritter wrote in great detail a century ago, though on an entirely different basis. In chapter VI we shall revert to Ritter's ideas.)

We will try to elucidate these pronouncements with an example. A particular chorological differentiation of the climate, such as a high annual temperature and great humidity in the Amazone area, is important for a particular chorological variation of the organic world, namely for the micro-flora and the micro-fauna in this area. The significance of this climate for the microbiosphere of this area is geographically important, if these micro-organisms are important to the human inhabitants of the Amazone area. This land is consequently looked upon as the world, as the specific home of those people.

Hartshorne's statement that geography considers the earth as the world of man requires some further explanation. It is clear with respect to the earth in its natural condition, just as our example of the importance to man of the climate and the biosphere in the Amazone area needs no further elucidation. But geography is not only concerned with the phenomena of the nature of the earth in its importance to man, and not only with the physical, chemical and organic phenomena of the earth as the world of and for man. Geography studies the *totality* of the material and immaterial complex of the earth in its chorological diversity. What about this totality as the world of man? If we understand Hartshorne properly, he also refers to this totality, for he says: "Any phenomenon, whether of nature or of man is significant in geography to the extent and degree to which its interrelation with other phenomena . . .

40

determines ... the totality of areal variation, measured in respect to significance to man" [23].

This pronouncement is not entirely clear, and we think further explanation necessary. For this further interpretation we are responsible. We maintain the complex of material and immaterial things, of nature and man, as world in its significance to man. At first sight it looks as if this implies a contradiction. How is it possible to speak of a world in its importance to man if this world already comprises things and phenomena of man? We are of opinion, however, that this contradiction is only apparent, not real. In thought we consider the earthly complex of material and immaterial things as a reality outside of man, and inquire into the significance of this complex to man as the principal inhabitant of the earth. What is the significance of this complex in connection with the fact that the earth is the world of man?

We consider man's activities in their interrelation with nature, and ask: Are these integrations significant to the terrestrial world as the specific home of man? Does agriculture as the integration of economic thought, purpose, and action in relation with the soil, the climate, hydrography, vegetation, and culture have any significance to the earthly complex? Has the state as the integration of political activity in relation with the territory any significance to the earthly complex? This earthly complex is here looked upon as man's world, because man is the principal inhabitant of the earth.

Thus we posit the problem in a general way. In geography we further ask: Is the chorological differentiation of these integrations significant to the areas as the specific homes of their inhabitants? So we approach the material and the immaterial complex of an area from the standpoint of its human inhabitants. To these inhabitants this portion of the earth, this chorological differentiant is their world, which is distinguished from other areas, each of which is the world of its own inhabitants.

After the inquiry into the significance of the chorological differentiations another problem should be discussed: Are there any

41

important vertical integrations of chorological differentiations in different places which are so closely related that they can be included in the same class? And if so, is it, generally speaking, possible to divide the vertical chorologically varying complex according to important integrations which differ essentially as well as in kind?

We have already discussed many related integrations of different places on earth. Arable farming, dairy farming and pasture cattle-breeding, horticulture and industrial regions are chorologically differentiated integrations which are so closely related that we can speak of similarity of kind. This similarity of kind consists in the fact that various phenomena that vary chorologically are interrelated with the chorologically differentiated economic phenomena. These integrations have the economic element in common. They differ from those integrations in which the political phenomenon, or the purely cultural phenomenon is the common element. There are also integrations of nature that are similar, e.g., the chorological differentiations of the natural vegetation of different places that are interrelated with the chorological differentiations of climate, soil, hydrography and other natural elements. In them vegetation is the common element.

Many integrations are reducible to the same kind, and they are essentially different from others that are included in another class. Is the difference between the integrations that we have called an essential difference, really so important in a geographical sense? We think it is. Geographical science has developed forms of geography that are based on this difference, such as economic, political, cultural, and social geography, plant geography, zoogeography, pedological geography, climatic geography and some other forms of geography.

The economic, political, social and cultural phenomena, the plants, the animals, the soils, climates and waters are significant to the world in its function as the home of the most important inhabitant of the earth, viz., man. Observation and investigation soon showed that the separate phenomena are interrelated with the other phenomena, but each in a different way. The knowledge of other countries acquired drew the attention to the

42

chorological diversity of the elements. At first only the chorological differentiation of separate things was noticed, but on closer investigation also the integration of these chorological variations came to light. Not all terrestrial things and phenomena that are significant to man vary in a chorological respect to an equal degree, and not all chorological differentiations display a large measure of integration. But the different forms of geography we have just mentioned point the way for the analysis of the chorologically varying complex of earthly things and phenomena. The entire complex is to be analysed into a number of separate integrations, each of which is separately called *a unity of totality*. Each unity has a definite structure and the component elements have a function with respect to each other. Within every unity of totality there is one nuclear element to which the other elements are related as influences. Investigation has to show which of the elements have greater or less significance to the nucleus, the principal element. As we are confronted with an integration of elements (terrestrial things and phenomena) that show chorological variations, such a unity of totality can be looked upon as a geographic unity of totality. Again, this unity can be further defined as a *vertical unity of geographic totality,* because it bears on the differentiations found in the same locality [24].

Every unity of totality or integration has geographic significance if it is chorologically differentiated, and if this integration is important for the whole earthly complex, which is considered to be the world of man, a world in which man is the principal inhabitant. This also holds for a physical-geographic totality. Particular physical phenomena differentiating chorologically and influenced by dissimilar differentiations, together constitute an integration. This integration is geographically significant if it is important for the earth surface, which is the world of man.

When we consider the chorologically differentiated phenomena in their significance to the areas, which areas are the specific homes of the different human groups, it will be clear that the integrations (unities of totality) of physical geography and of biogeography are less independent than those of anthropo-geography. The former two kinds of integrations in which a physical or a biotic

43

element is the nucleus, are as a whole again related to man, the principal inhabitant. In the anthropo-geographic integrations the nucleus is already a human element to which other elements, differentiated phenomena, are immediately related.

In a vertical economic-geographic totality the economic element is the nucleus, the principal differentiation to which the other chorological differentiations are related as influences. In a vertical politico-geographic totality the political element is the nucleus on which the other chorological differentiations exert their influence. In pedological geography and in morphology the ground, the soil and the forms of the ground are the nucleus round which the other chorological differentiations are arranged.

Within the various unities of geographic totality very often the same elements, the same differentiations are found, but their functions are very different and their totality structures are different. In a vertical economic-geographic totality the economic element is the nucleus, the soil is an influence, a sphere of operation with regard to the economic element. In the vertical pedological-geographic totality the soil is the nucleus and the economic element acts as a determining factor on this soil via human labour. The structure and function of the two totalities are different. In the former there are particular cultural elements which are immediately significant to the economic nucleus; in the latter these elements are less important for the soil as a nucleus and in many cases their influence is indirect, via the economic element. The latter element is very important in the pedologic-geographic totality, because human labour exercises a considerable influence on the composition of the soil owing to manuring and the regulation of the water supply.

In the economic-geographic totality of an agricultural region the problem is posited as follows: What is the influence of the relevant differentiation of the soil on the economic differentiation? Then we ask what influence is exercised by the economic element on the soil in so far as the effects of this influence are in their turn significant to the economic element. Thus, e.g. at a particular point of time in a particular area agriculture has to do with a particular kind of soil of a given structure. The question is, what influence is

44

exerted by this soil on economic life, i.e., what possibility offered by the soil has been utilized by the farmer? Next the question is raised as to how the farmer works this soil in connection with the use of the soil, and what are the effects on the farmer's economic life. (When we speak of "the farmer", we mean the average agriculturist in this agricultural region.)

Although in a vertical geographic totality there is question of a nuclear differentiation to which other differentiations are related as influences, this totality is a functionally interrelated integration. But in this functional integration we are ultimately especially concerned with the influence of the other differentiations on the nuclear differentiation. For in the economic geographic totality just mentioned the problem is: what is the influence of the soil on economic life? Next we ask, what is the influence the farmer exercises on the soil on account of his cultivation of the soil? But in the latter case the issue is concerned with the economic effects of a particular method of working the soil. The interrelationships are, therefore, investigated from the viewpoint of a particular way of positing the problem, in which the economic differentiation is the nucleus.

In the economic-geographic totality there is mostly a certain amount of law-conformity which has a conditional and functional character. In the pedological-geographic totality there is rather a strong physical causality discernible in the process of the influence of the economic element on the soil. The process of thinking and considering which precedes the farmer's labour, his particular way of cultivating the soil, is, however, not governed by physical causality.

Within the geographical complex there are, consequently, different vertical unities of geographic totality to be distinguished. But also within one and the same geographic totality of different places the integration and the significance of the different characteristics of the different things are very dissimilar. The economic-geographic totality of agriculture in a particular area of the old China and that of an area in the Great Plains are very different in structure as well as in function, as has been explained above. Differences in the socio-economic order, in local or interlocal economy, in the quality and

45

quantity of technique, the application of animate energy or fund energy, differences in density of population, are as many factors that determine the significance of the different characteristics of the various things and their integration. And yet the two vertical interrelations are similar. For in both integrations of the two areas we are concerned with economic life as it is related to other things and phenomena in these areas. The structure and the function of economic life, however, are different. The significance of the different characteristics of the different things which are significant to economic life, varies with the nature of economic life. But both integrations are chorological differentiations of a similar character. Both integrations belong to the economic-geographic totality.

The same thing occurs within the economic-geographic totality of an area at different times. An agricultural region in which formerly the clay soil was used for growing sugar-beets and wheat, had an economic-geographic totality of a different structure, and often also with a different function, from that of this region at the present time, if pasture cattle-breeding is the means of living of the inhabitants.

Each of the different vertical unities of geographical totality, discovered by the analysis of the geographical complex, forms an integration of differentiations of definite things and phenomena as they occur at a particular point on the earth surface. As they are found at the same place, we have called this integration a vertical interrelation, in contra-distinction to the integration of the differentiations of different points or places of the earth surface that form a horizontal interconnection.

In the previous chapter we mentioned different regions: soil regions, vegetation regions, economic regions, etc. They were regions that were concerned with the surface extension of the chorological differentiation of the separate things and phenomena. Even though we discussed the question as to what other chorological differentiations influenced them, these regions chiefly referred to the chorological differentiation of separate things.

After establishing the various geographical totalities we now concentrate on the problem about the uniform extension of the

46

surface of these vertical geographic totalities, i.e., the regions that constitute these integrations of vertically interrelated differentiations. As we are concerned here with the uniform extension of a totality of differentiations, and not only with that of one differentiation, we are considering a geographical region and not merely a region: an economic-geographical region, a cultural-geographical region, a plant-geographical region, a pedological-geographical region, etc. We speak of *the vertical unity of region*, if there is a uniform extension of the interrelated differentiations of a definite vertical geographic totality *.

Although every geographical region is not only determined by the uniform surface extension of the vertically interrelated differentiations, but also by the horizontal interconnection, we will first study the extension of this vertical integration. For the vertical interrelation of the differentiations in uniform extension is immediately manifest in our experience and this is the primary thing in the chorological differentiation. The horizontal interconnection binding these vertical integrations of different places and also the separate differentiations of different places more or less into a relative unity, will be discussed in a later context.

The problem is: what about the uniform surface extension of the vertically interrelated differentiations forming a geographical region?

Although one thing and one phenomenon may be said to show greater chorological variation than another, and the same thing may have widely different variations at different places on earth within a definite distance, it should be stated that the chorological differentiation is in reality infinite.

A territory indicated by referring to its young sea clay soil, does

* In this study we usually speak of a region as a "unity", and of "regional unity". We generally avoid the designation of a region as a "unit", and as a "regional unit". To our mind the concept "unit" has a more accurate and exact connotation than that of "unity". As the homogeneity of a region cannot be determined in such a sharp and exact way — this homogeneity exists only in certain respects — we prefer the term "unity".

47

not have a perfectly identical physical structure and chemical composition even over a very short distance. Only at a point on earth is the chorological differentiation uniform. Rational knowledge operates, however, with concepts combining characteristics which indicate the essential nature of a thing. Similar things that differ individually are comprehended in one concept on the ground of the similarity in their essential characteristics. Thus with the aid of concepts we can speak of a chorological differentiation of the soil, and distinguish the latter into peat, young and old sea clay, sand etc. and indicate the extension as a peat region, a sea clay and a sandy region, etc. respectively. The size of the region, however, is also determined with the aid of the standards we apply to the chorological differentiation. In a special investigation of a portion of the world a distinction will be made between an arable farming and a cattle-breeding region, which can be distinguished as two adjoining chorological differentiants. A geography of the world, however, will often ignore these differentiations, and consider this portion of the world as one chorological differentiant, as one agrarian region.

Any given piece of the world is a chorological differentiant. It differs from any other piece of the world. But not every given piece is an essential chorological differentiant.

Let us imagine an area of which the western part has arable land, the centre has pasture cattle-breeding and the east horticulture and industry, the industrial part lying apart from and to the east of the horticultural part. We might e.g. distinguish three economic-geographical regions *: a region consisting of arable farms and part of the pasture cattle-breeding land; another region combining the other part of the cattle-breeding farms and an adjoining part of horticulture; and lastly a region consisting of the remaining part of horticulture and the adjoining industry. These are three economic-geographic regions; they are chorological differentiations. They can be distinguished from each other and according to definite special characteristics they differ from any other piece of the world.

* The term region here is only a preliminary indication.

48

Each of these geographical regions has vertically interrelated differentiations of material and immaterial things and phenomena. There is vertical interrelation in every small locality, but the regions lack vertical unity, because within every region there is no uniform extension of the interrelated differentiations. One region contains agriculture and pasture cattle-breeding; in the second there is pasture cattle-breeding and horticulture, and in the third there is horticulture and industry. The difference between these regions is not maximal, because particular characteristics are the same in different regions. Both the first and the second region partly contain pasture cattle-breeding. The second and the third partly have both horticulture. The structure and function of the interrelated chorological differentiations in each of the geographical regions are not homogeneous, because they are mixed and not uniform. The economic-geographic regions that we have distinguished are no essential economic-geographic regions; they are no pure chorological differentiations, because the difference between them is not maximal. The chorological diversity is not essential, because the difference between the geographical regions is not as great as it possibly can be in this case. For, if this portion of the world is divided into four economic-geographical regions: an arable farm region, a pasture cattle-breeding region, a horticultural region, and an industrial region, there will be four essential chorological differentiants, each of which is homogeneous and uniform in extension. The difference, the chorological differentiation, will be maximal. It goes without saying that this uniformity has been determined in accordance with certain essential standards applied by the investigator.

Let us now suppose, however, that the three regions we have mentioned first, coalesce with three civil municipalities. Then they are not arbitrary from the point of view of civil administration. From a politico-geographical standpoint they will be three essential chorological differentiants. (The concept "political", as it is intended here in a specially geographic sense, refers to the civil administration and government.) These two examples show that a particular portion of the world contains essential chorologically differentiated integrations that do not coalesce. The uniform surface extension of the four separate vertical economic-geographical integrations does not coalesce with that of the three vertical politico-geographical integrations, i.e., the chorological differentiation of the economic-geographical totality and that of the politico-geographical totality are different. An economic-geographical region is not identical with a politico-geographical region. This also holds for other integrations. Suppose that from West to East the soil consists of clay, peat, and sand, and the respective boundaries run across the cattle-breeding region and the horticultural region, but they do not coalesce with the boundaries of the three civil municipalities. Then the three pedological-geographic regions overlap the two other kinds of geographical regions *.

Geographical regions should be essential chorological differentiations of a definite integration that can be pointed out in the earthly reality. For in this case the issue is not the determination of ideal types (Idealtypen). To a certain extent our geographical regions, too, are abstractions. For in a geographical region, formed according to a particular integration, there are also other integrations, whose geographical regions do not coalesce with the former one, but overlap it to a greater or lesser extent. We shall revert to the nature of these abstractions in a later context.

Geographical regions should represent the maximum chorological differentiation found in a particular integration of earthly

---

* In connection with this, however, we must point out that in the near future we can expect a larger unity of economic-geographic and politico-geographic (administrative-geographic) regions in different parts of the world. Present regional planning (town and country-planning) on the part of the government is concerned with a comprehensive complex of things in a larger or smaller region. The planning comprises economic activities, land policy, the housing of the working classes, the regulation of the ground water level and of the water supply, cultural and social activities, together with recreation. As far as the Netherlands are concerned, the planning will be carried out in the smaller regions by the municipalities in cooperation with the drainage boards and the provincial authorities; in the larger regions the provincial authorities will take the lead in close cooperation with the national government.

Also the change in the various municipal boundaries, the combination of small municipalities, and the annexation of small municipalities by large ones in connection with regional planning and with development schemes point to it that in the future the regions of many municipalities will perhaps form a unity of a more comprehensive totality.

reality. If the differentiation, the difference, is maximal, the surface extension will also be maximal. In the example we have just discussed, the pasture cattle-breeding region *as a whole* is a vertical unity. A part of the pasture cattle-breeding region is not a vertical unity, not a geographical region, because this part is not distinguishable from other parts of this pasture cattle-breeding region. It is not a chorological differentiant within this cattle-breeding region. The cattle-breeding region as a whole is a vertical unity, a geographical region, viz., a chorological differentiant distinguishable from the adjoining arable region, the horticultural and the industrial region.

Geography does not want to establish an arbitrary chorological differentiation of the world, but an essential diversity; no more does historical science wish to make an arbitrary division in the course of the whole of history, but a division into periods which each of them constitutes a homogeneous length of time which is essentially different from other periods.

We have distinguished the complex of earthly things into different unities of geographical totality: an economic-geographical, a politico-geographical, a pedological-geographical totality, etc. In the total complex of a point on earth there are simultaneously different geographical totalities to be found. Particular totalities, such as the economic-geographical integration, should be more exactly defined. The latter integration must be further distinguished into the geographical totality of agriculture, or into that of industry, or of some other economic-geographical totality. The geographical integration of agriculture is again further distinguished into that of arable farming, cattle-breeding, horticulture or forestry. It is evident that such further distinction and determination depends on the purpose of our investigation, and on the standards of differentiation we apply.

If this distinction, this further definition, comprises essential integrations, it is important to determine the regions of this integration in such a way that the surface extension is homogeneous and unmixed. Such uniformity and homogeneity may be simple or compound: an agricultural region may consist of farms of the same type with mono-culture, but also of similar farms with the same but multifarious crops.

Every piece of the world is a reflection of the world as a whole, says Von Humboldt [25]. We would add to this thesis: not every piece of the world is an essential chorological differentiant of the world. Any given piece of the earth surface, any area consists of a diversity of geographic regions, — each of these regions being an essential chorological differentiant. These regions, however, very often overlap.

In order to gain an insight into the chorological diversity within a particular vertical unity of totality it is necessary to make essential distinctions between the geographical regions of this particular geographical totality. Homogeneous uniform geographical regions are the clearest representations of the chorological diversity of the world within a particular geographical totality. Then it is possible to gain an insight into the unity and the whole formed by the various geographical regions of the world within this vertical geographical totality. The same thing is true for the study of the entire interrelated complex of differentiations in one part of the world. Then, too, it is necessary to determine the uniform surface extension of each important integration of differentiations, so as to establish the composition of the complex of an area.

It is clear that when we speak of the uniform chorological extension of the geographical region of an integration, it is intended in a figurative sense. In a literal sense an integration or an interrelation has no dimensions. It is the things that are differentiated which have dimensions. These differentiations are interrelated, form an integration, and in this sense we speak of the geographical region of an integration.

However, we should bear in mind that the uniform chorological extension of economic-geographical integrations is often very strongly interrupted. This causes great difficulties when the various economic-geographical regions must be determined. In the rural areas of the Netherlands with their smaller exporting industry which has no catering function for the surrounding agrarian land, this is even more emphatically so. The actual state of affairs here often shows the interchange over a short distance of an agrarian-geographical integration with an industrial-geographical integration.

In the above we have demonstrated by means of the examples of economic-geographical, politico-geographical and pedological-geographical regions of a part of the world that the structure and the function of these vertical geographical totalities are different. A particular differentiation in its uniform chorological extension is the nucleus in one vertical integration to which the others are related as influences, in another integration this same differentiation is an influence on another nucleus. Although all these differentiations of the entire complex influence each other to a greater or lesser degree, they do not vary or differentiate in the same way in a chorological sense (in surface extension), because the primary causes of the chorological differentiation of the various things and phenomena are most often different. Hartshorne [26] distinguishes the following natural things which vary in a semi-independent way: the distribution of land and water on the earth, the form and the relief of the ground, the structure of the soil, the chemical composition of the parent rock, the mineral deposit, the temperature of the atmosphere, and the precipitation (rain, sleet, snow, etc.). Many human things are added to them.

Let us consider temperature and precipitation. The chorological differentiation of the temperature is in the first place the result of the differentiation of the angle of incidence of the sun-beams and of the duration of the irradiation. They are, each in a different way, dependent on the differences in geographical latitude. Owing to the differentiation in temperature, on account of the differences in temperature of the various places, there arise vertical and horizontal air-streams. They determine the further differentiation of the temperature and also that of the precipitation. But the two climatic elements vary in a different way in connection with this atmospheric circulation. The differentiation of temperature and precipitation is further also determined, although in a different way again, by the alternation of land and sea, by the differences between the eastern and the western side of the continents, and by the differences in form and altitude of the land. The differentiations of temperature and precipitation influence each other also. So

with respect to temperature we may say that the variation in geographical latitude is the primary cause of the chorological differentiation of temperature. All the other factors mentioned, however,
are also more or less important for the chorological differentiation
of temperature. Hence we can say: the variation in temperature is
semi-independent of the variation of precipitation.

In an earlier context we have observed that the influence of
particular things on other things may be so strong that the original
dissimilarity in their differentiation will vanish. The influence of
the climate on the soils is an example. Owing to the process of
weathering the differentiation of the upper layers of the soil follows
that of the climate. But the deeper layers of the soil do not vary in
the same way.

Greater still is the influence of man's action with respect to the
soil, vegetation, and hydrography. Man's economic aims are so
much directive that many differentiations that did not have same
uniform surface extension originally, now coalesce.

When one tries to determine the region of a vertical integration
of differentiations it will be clear that its uniformity and homogeneity are only limited. Not all the differentiations included in the
integration have the same uniform surface extension. The limita-
tions obtaining here are essentially the same as those that are valid
for the differentiations of the entire complex. And yet the uniformity
and homogeneity of a separate integration are greater than those
of the whole complex. For not all the elements of the complex
have been included in a particular integration. Besides it is particular
characteristics of the elements that play a rôle. The latter circumstance is very important. The chorological differentiation of the
terrestrial complex forms geographic regions. They are, however,
no individuals who exist separately. In proportion as the characteristics of the elements of an integration are significant for determining the chorological differentiation, the chorological extension of
the differentiations of the elements can be different. Let us consider
the element "soil" in an economic-geographic integration. For
the chorological differentiation of this vertical integration the
difference in agriculture, pasture cattle-breeding etc., is decisive.
If an area is characterized by the uniform extension of a pasture

cattle-breeding region, but its soil consists of clay, low peat and sand, there is still a reason to speak of the uniformity of the form of production, viz., pasture cattle-breeding. The uniformity of the soil is to be called interrupted on account of the characteristics we attribute to the element "soil" from a definite pedological viewpoint. On the ground of these characteristics there is a chorological differentiation of the soil of this area, e.g., the west consists of clay, the centre of low peat, and the east of sand. But these characteristics are not decisive of pasture cattle-breeding. The difference between clay, peat and sand is not determinative but a certain degree of similarity of these soils. Soils denoted by the names clay, peat and sand do not differ in every respect. In certain respects all three are podzolic soils. In our example they are *pasture soils* in which especially the regulation of the ground water level and the water supply are very important, because they make grass vegetation possible. The uniform extension of this integration, the pasture cattle-breeding region is not interrupted by the difference in clay, sand and low peat. The same thing applies to the climate in an economic-geographic integration in which either the uniform extension of a particular differentiation of temperature, or that of moisture, may be decisive. The chorological differentiations of these two do not coalesce. The one may be uniform over a long distance, whereas the other is more markedly differentiated. Then the nature of the integration is decisive, e.g., the question as to whether the climate is concerned with cultivated crops or with natural vegetation.

In every vertical interrelation there is one differentiation that functions as its nucleus to which other differentiations are related as influences. A geographic region, the uniform extension of an integration, is in the first place determined by the uniform extension of the nuclear differentiation. Next it is ascertained what other differentiations are of importance for this nucleus, and what is the surface extension of these differentiations. In addition, continuous attention must be given to the functional coherence of the integration: whether the functional coherence of the differentiations has a uniform extension or whether it shows any changes. The differen-tiations form an integration at every point of the earth. This integration or unity of totality is also determining for the differentiations. It has the character of a whole which determines the differentiations at every point of the earth as its parts. This means that the differentiation of a thing is determined according to certain characteristics. On account of the chorological differentiation of these characteristics we speak of the chorological differentiation of this thing. But this thing is a part of an integration; the characteristics of this thing that are significant consequently depend on the structure and the function of the integration.

The determination of the geographical region of a vertical integration or totality requires the harmony of an analysis and a synthesis. The geographical region is determined by the uniform chorological extension of the integration, for which the uniform extension of the nuclear differentiation and the differentiations that are of the greatest importance for the nucleus, is the standard. The differentiations that are of minor importance in the integration and which more or less deviate from the region of the nuclear differentiation in their chorological extension are less important for determining the geographical region of the integration.

It will be clear that the greater the number is of differentiated phenomena included in an integration, the smaller the vertical region will be in otherwise identical circumstances. For however great the importance of the integration as a whole may be for the component phenomena, and however strong the influence of a particular phenomenon may be on other phenomena within an integration, there is partial semi-independent differentation of these phenomena. That is to say that over equal distances the chorological differentiation increases if the integration comprises more phenomena. The uniform chorological extension (the geographic region) of an integration decreases as the complexity of the integration increases; they are, as it were, inversely proportionate to each other.

In certain areas it is often very difficult to determine the geographic region of an integration of vertically interrelated differentiations. This holds especially for the economic-geographic totality, which is often very complicated, and, although the component differentiations are closely interrelated, the uniform chorological

56

extension of particular groups of component phenomena is different. In such a case it is difficult to tell which groups of phenomena are more or less important in the integration. Recall areas on either side of the frontier between two states. Soil, climate, water supply position, together with the nature and form of the production are often very similar. These phenomena constitute an economic-geographic integration which has a uniform extension in which the political frontier disturbs the unity of the region. But in other respects there is after all a very profound difference in economic life. This difference is due to the fact that the two regions on either side of the frontier belong to two different states. The different purchasing power of the money, the difference in the provisions of the law and in the regulations laid down by the state with reference to, e.g., imports and exports, the establishing of industries, and the difference in taxes form differentiations. Such matters are also important in an economic-geographic integration. From this viewpoint the uniform chorological extension of the economic-geographic region is not continued at the political frontier, and we speak of the differentiation into two economic-geographic regions. These regions are sharply separated by the frontier between the two states.

It is clear that except in the case of politico-geographic integrations such as states, municipalities and provinces the geographic regions of the various integrations are not separated by sharp limits but very often gradually merge into one another. Then we speak of transitional regions, regions of a fading character, which may have a very different extension.

If we want to examine an area according to its peculiarity by which it is distinguishable from adjoining areas, and we discuss all the integrations of the complex, it is necessary to determine the extent and the form of such an area "provisionally" according to a particular characteristic of this area. For this purpose one may use, e.g., the characteristics of the soil, if the area concerned has a soil that differs from that of the surrounding areas. In this area there are several distinct integrations of phenomena of nature and culture to be found which partly overlap. The problem to be discussed is whether there is an integration which has priority, so that the geographic region of this integration is decisive of the definitive chorological extension and delimitation of the area.

In general we would call that integration the most fundamental which has the closest vertical interrelation of its component differentiations, and which comprises the greatest number of differentiations, provided this integration is also more important for man as the principal inhabitant of that area. The latter requirement, however, is the most difficult condition, although the former factors are also very complicated. Theoretically, however, it is possible to take the view that by means of a very accurate investigation the comprehension and the intensity of an integration can be determined. It is perhaps not possible to ascertain what integration is more important in connection with its significance to the area as the home of its inhabitants without the investigator's view of life playing its rôle.

Let us consider an area which has an old sea clay soil. In the western part arable farming strongly prevails, in the eastern part pasture cattle-breeding and dairy farming is the means of subsistence. From a pedological standpoint the soil is the same in both, but shows a difference in the level of the soil water which is regulated by two drainage boards in connection with the different requirements of agriculture and pasturage. The arable farmers are Roman-Catholics, the live stock owners of the greater portion of the eastern part of the area are Protestants. But a smaller portion of the livestock owners in the centre of the area is Roman-Catholic. The home of these Roman-Catholic stock owners directly adjoins the living area of the Roman-Catholic arable farmers. The Roman-Catholic live stock owners cooperate with the Protestant live stock owners in a cooperative dairy factory and in the management of the polder for the regulation of the soil water level and other hydrological matters. The Roman-Catholic arable farmers supply their sugar beets to the sugar factory in their region and manage their polder. But the Roman-Catholic live stock owners cooperate with the Roman-Catholic arable farmers in the social, religious, and cultural spheres in a Roman-Catholic farmers' union, in schools, a church and in simple cultural institutions, the greater part of

58

which are found within the arable region. The Protestant live stock owners have churches, schools and cultural centres in their region and are united in a protestant farmers' union.

So in this area there are two economic-geographic regions and two cultural-geographic regions that do not coalesce but overlap each other in the centre of this area *. In addition, this area belongs to three civil municipalities. Only with respect to the soil is it one region. The soil water level is indeed different in each of them, but from the standpoint of pedology this is no sufficient reason for distinguishing two soil regions. In our opinion the economic-geographic and the cultural-geographic integrations are the most important. They are comprehensive and intensive, but they do not coalesce. There remains one difficulty for a definitive determination of this piece of the world, for which it is necessary to distinguish two areas instead of one: This is the question how to determine the boundary between the two areas, because the two most important integrations overlap. Which integration is more important for the two areas as the living spaces of the human inhabitants? The decision to be taken is probably dependent on the investigator's view of life. In our opinion it will be necessary from a geographical point of view to lay the stress on the integration in which the elements of the nature, especially the ground have the greatest importance. This is probably the economic-geographic integration. But whatever decision is taken, it will never be entirely satisfactory. One of the two integrations, and also the other integration mentioned, do not form homogeneous uniform regions within the two regions of the integration to which priority has been given, although such homogeneous uniform regions are really there. They can only be realized at the expense of the other integrations. An area is usually not a perfect unity with regard to all its vertical integrations.

We can, of course say that there is a smaller area, which forms the nuclear region which the various geographic regions have in common owing to their overlapping. This central area forms a vertical chorogical unity of all the integrations. It is a homogeneous

* We speak of cultural-geographic regions because the socio-cultural phenomena are considered to be the nucleus to which the religious phenomena are related.

59

region. But then the different parts of the area falling outside of the centre must be ignored, although they embrace important integrations. This procedure is unacceptable. For the chorological differentiation such a nuclear region is of no importance. For many important integrations the nuclear region is no chorological differentiant because the phenomena of this central region are similar to those lying immediately beyond the nuclear region. The chorological differentiation is arbitrary then. There is no longer any question of essential chorological diversity, because there is no maximal difference and no maximal chorological extension of the chorological differentiations.

So if we want to mark off an area, we shall have to decide which integration is the most important for us and is to be the standard of chorological differentiation by means of which we can distinguish the area from adjoining areas according to its size and its boundaries.

The difficulty of establishing which integration in its chorological extension is the most important and should determine the size, the form and the limits of an area, however, in reality is less great for a geographer who studies the area. A geographer, like any other scientist, is limited in his mental possibilities. Only very few of them are able to go deeply into all the vertical integrations. The normal investigator will chiefly have to restrict his efforts to a single integration, if his work is not to be frustrated by superficiality. Then he will determine an area according to the geographic region of that vertical integration whose phenomena he knows about and into which he has an insight owing to his professional study and his personal interest. This restriction is all the more necessary if we bear in mind that he is concerned with the speciality of an integration of an area as it is distinct from that of other, above all adjoining areas. To know this speciality it is necessary to know integrations of the same kind of other areas from which the integration in question can be distinguished.

Finally we wish to say something about the structure and the function of the geographical region formed by a vertical unity of integration (totality).

We have repeatedly mentioned the structure and the function

60

of a vertical integration or totality. But this is not the same thing as the structure and the function of the region formed by the integration. At every point on earth an integration has a structure and a function. The former has the build of a whole embracing the differentiations as its parts. The function is formed by the mutual actions of the differentiations and by the action of the whole on the differentiations separately. The structure is the same from one point of the earth to the other within this geographic region. It is clear that the entire region of the integration has this structure. When, however, we speak of function within a geographic region as a vertical unity, there is only question of the same function of the integration at all its earth points. However, the interconnections between the things of different earth points within a region and the interconnections of the region as a whole with adjoining or remote regions are horizontal relations. This function is not vertical but horizontal, a circumstance that we shall discuss later on.

Is a geographic region of vertical integration something real? It is reality insofar as this geographic region can be pointed out as a piece of the world of a definite size, form and position in which this vertical integration of differentiations is to be found in uniform chorological extension. But this piece of the world has been determined by us according to that one vertical integration. In reality this integration is interwoven with other integrations, which together form the entire earthly complex of an area. The other vertical integrations have different uniform chorological extensions. In most cases the geographical regions of these distinct vertical integrations overlap each other. The administrative-geographical region, the economic-geographical region, and the pedological-geographical region in a part of the world usually do not coalesce.

In a certain sense the geographical region of a vertical integration has been abstracted from a complex. It has been considered apart. In reality it only exists within the total complex of a part of the world with which it is interwoven, and which in its turn is a part of the earth surface, of the world as a whole. But this part of the world, or this area, can be pointed out. It forms a unity, but only a unity on the ground of definite interrelated phenomena. The unity has been formed according to a limited integration of differentiations. This area is a reality, but it is only a chorological unity in a certain respect. This respect has been determined according to a part of reality, which part does not exist separately in reality.

Hartshorne speaks of geographical regions as "mental constructions" and of an "intellectual framework" [27].

Schmitthenner says: A geographic unity is based on the standpoint of its factors (faktoriellen Gesichtspunkt) and formed according to a constructional principle (Konstruktionsprinzip). In another passage he speaks of the unity of a region as of a "construction (Setzung) of the investigator" [28].

To a certain extent a geographical region is a form of thought [29]. But it is a necessary construction to gain an insight into the complicated reality. It shows a certain amount of similarity to the abstractions of the systematic sciences. For the economic, the political, the social and the cultural elements can be distinguished but not really be separated. The same thing holds for the elements of nature.

When we compare the different forms of chorological differentiation we have defined in this and in the preceding chapter, we get the apparently remarkable result that the more we abstract from the chorological complex, the better we are able to distinguish the chorological unities that are determined by the differentiation.

When we direct our attention to the chorological differentiation of one thing or one phenomenon, and consider this separately, we have made a fairly strong abstraction. For a single thing and its chorological differentiation are in reality interwoven with the entire complex of things. The regions, however, formed of this thing on the ground of its chorological differentiation can be distinguished pretty accurately on earth. True, the boundaries of these regions are not sharp as a rule. There are often more or less wide strips of a transitional character. But for the rest these regions can be accurately pointed out, and in proportion as finer standards are applied, the size of these regions steadily decreases.

When we consider this thing in relation to other things by which it is influenced, we shall obtain a definite integration, a vertical unity of totality. This integration still bears the character of an abstraction, for in reality this integration is interlaced with other integrations, but we are closer to reality than when we consider an individual thing. The geographical regions determined on the ground of the chorological differentiation of the integration, can still be ascertained and pointed out on the earth, but this distinction already requires further reflection on that which is of more or of less importance in the integration. The unity, the uniform chorological extension is restricted to the nuclear differentiation and to those differentiations by which the nuclear differentiation is influenced most, and which are the most closely interrelated differentiations with the nucleus.

If we direct our investigation to the entire complex of things and phenomena, we have to do with full reality. There are, however, no unities of chorological differentiation distinguishable in this complicated reality. With the exception of small islands, which are sometimes an approach to unities of total differentiation, there are no areas in the world which are uniform unities.

The regions of separate things and of the integrations of things are not the same. They overlap and fit into the continuum of the world, but they do not reflect this continuum as a reality. The vertical chorological differentiation of the whole of the earthly complex is a reality but does not form unities of region.

Apparently this state of affairs is a remarkable one, but on closer investigation it is logical. The further we go with the analysis of the complicated reality and consider things and phenomena separately, the sharper the picture can be. The picture becomes clearer but at the same time it becomes more unreal. This, however, is only natural, and is implied in our aim. To gain an insight we must make the picture, i.e. our picture, more distinct. To make the picture sharper we have to analyse and to isolate things and phenomena in a greater or lesser degree. The chorai that we form become clearer and sharper and can be better distinguished on the earth. So we have reached our aim. But we overshoot our mark if we do not constantly realize that we have simplified reality in a high degree. For this purpose it is always necessary for us to try to synthetize the different pictures and to confront them with reality.

CHAPTER IV

GEOTOPES AND VERTICAL
CHOROLOGICAL UNITIES

The various things and their phenomena constituting the earthly complex are often differentiated, or varied in chorologically different ways, and within a certain distance the same thing is often differentiated to a greater or lesser degree in different localities of the earth surface. The various vertical integrations or totalities of these differentiations often do not have the same chorological extension in the same part of the world and overlap each other. If the whole complex of the chorological differentiations of an area must be described, this area must be determined according to its chorological boundaries by means of a compromise of the different geographical regions of the various integrations that overlap. It is true, one vertical integration embraces more differentiations than another, or shows a stronger interrelation than another, and one is also more important for the earth as the world of man than another. In our opinion, however, it will always be necessary to compromise, if we wish to determine the chorological unity of the whole complex of an area. This determination is influenced by the investigator's evaluation. This subjective element of evaluation is already there when the investigator decides upon the standard to be used for the differentiation of each separate phenomenon, and inquires how great the quantitative and the qualitative difference must be to entitle him to speak of chorological differentiation.

And yet there are various geographers who suppose that in earthly reality there are small chorological units which may be used as objective standards for the determination of geographic regions, and perhaps even for the determination of the chorological units of the whole earthly complex.

Particularly in Germany many geographers have carried out important investigations in this field. They are especially Paffen, Schmithüsen and Troll, who have been engaged in the examination of small earth spaces. Troll [1] says: "We speak of 'Kleinste Landschaftsindividuen' or 'Kleinlandschaften' when in their further spatial division (Aufgliederung) there are a plurality of different units of location (Standortseinheiten) which are ecologically homogeneous in themselves, and which we call 'Ökotope' or 'Landschaftszellen'. They occur in a very definite assortment and in a characteristic combination (Landschaftskomplex), and in a definite pattern of distribution (Landschaftsmuster, Landschaftsmosaik, landscapepattern) they form a 'Kleinlandschaft'."

Schmithüsen [2] distinguishes between "Fliese" and "Ökotop". The former is only a physico-topographical unit, the latter is a physico-biotic topographical unit. Both units are viewed in their ecological locative significance (Standortsbedeutung). In our opinion Paffen has rightly raised objections to the motives on which Schmithüsen's distinctions are based. He says: The soil is a complex from which the biotic aspect cannot be eliminated without changing the ecology of a locality completely. In the case of anorganic natural landscapes in extremely dry and cold areas, where the biotic element is lacking in the soil complex, the concept "Fliese" as a non-biotic complex is meaningless as to its character of the habitat of living beings. According to Paffen there is, properly speaking no question here of a habitat, the ecological value of nature for living beings is nil [3]. For such areas he uses the concept "Physiotop" as the topographical basic unit of an anorganic natural landscape. Consequently the term Physiotop does not refer to the ecological potential for living beings, "but simply proceeds from the spatial differentiation of natural economy resulting from non-biotic totality complexes" [4]. The topographical basic unit of an organic natural landscape Paffen calls Ökotop or Biotop, by which he means the same thing as Troll. An Ökotop is also the topographical basic unit of a cultivated landscape. By an Ökotop Troll and Paffen mean a topographical, natural-ecological homogeneous basic unit of a purely natural landscape and of a cultivated landscape which, as smallest landscape space in its homogeneous natural equipment, is the basis of the possibility of human use. In a pure cultivated landscape in which the soil has been intensively worked and changed by man, the natural composition and the chorological extension of an Ökotop has been so much changed that we can really no longer speak of an Ökotop. Then Paffen

65

speaks of a "Soziotop". "In their structure of interaction an Ökotop of a cultivated landscape (Kulturlandschafts-Ökotop), together with a Soziotop form the smallest basic cultivated landscape unit, which we would suggest to designate as a Geotop" [5]. All these topographical basic units Paffen comprises under the collective concept "Landschaftszelle". The smallest topographical basic units together form a "Kleinlandschaft", the smallest individual landscape.

Although Paffen and Troll would not identify a "Kleinlandschaft" with an organism built up of cells, they are of the opinion that the comparison with an organism is justified [6]. The "Landschaftszellen" are the building stones of a "Kleinlandschaft oder Teillandschaft". Paffen speaks of the structural unity and diversity of "Landschaftszellen" as well as of their relations based on their relative locations. Especially the relations based on relative location (Lagebeziehungen) of dissimilar Ökotope are very important for the ecological structure of a landscape (ökologischen Landschaftsgefüge) [7]. What the Ökotope or "Landschaftszellen" are to a "Kleinlandschaft", the various neighbouring "Kleinlandschaften" are to a larger unit, the "Einzellandschaft". This larger landscape unit, too, is not merely the sum total of a number of "Kleinlandschaften" but a "spatial ecological integration of the second stage of integration with its consequent greater spread of ecological homogeneity" [8].

In this way, via the decreasing homogeneity and uniformity, via the formal landscape pattern revealing the structure, via the ecological landscape dynamics constituting the function, Paffen again builds up larger units of landscape with a higher degree of integration, such as "Grosslandschaft, Grosslandschaftsgruppe, Landschaftsunterregion, Landschaftsregion, Landschaftsbereich, Landschaftszone, und Landschaftsgürtel" *.

When we now change over to our own terminology, retaining, however, Paffen's term landscape and space for clearness' sake,

---

* There is little sense in trying to translate these specifically German concepts, or in tracing the measure of agreement between them and the English geographical concepts "stow, stow-group, tract, tractgroup, sub-region, minor region, major region" [9].

66

we can say that in Paffen's landscape units both the vertical and the horizontal integrations play a rôle. As in connection with the fundamental principle of chorological differentiation we consider the vertical interrelation and unity to be of primary importance, we shall, therefore, first of all treat Paffen's ecological structure of action (ökologischer Wirkungsgefüge) of the smallest basic topographical unit and the homogeneity of a landscape and larger landscape units. In the next chapter, in which we shall explain the horizontal interconnection, we shall discuss the ecological structure of action and the dynamics of interaction existing between these smallest topographical units in a "Kleinlandschaft" and between the "Kleinlandschaften" of an "Einzellandschaft".

So an Ökotop is the smallest topographical basic unit. It is a complex of physico-chemical and biotic things including the hydrography and the atmosphere. It is not merely a piece of the ground with its groundwater and its ground climate, but also the water on the ground and the climate above the ground. The micro-climate, and the climate in the ordinary sense of the word, belong to the Ökotop [10]. With the flora and the fauna on the ground an Ökotop, which functions as a living-space, forms a biotic integration. In their turn flora and fauna influence the Ökotop, which therefore partly owes its properties to them. This ecological combined action forms a habitation in its significance for possible human use. Paffen considers this usability exlusively as the possibility offered by the complex for natural vegetation, or for the growth of cultivated crops destined either for animals or for human food. The significance of an Ökotop as the site for the establishment of industry is not discussed, except in a negative sense, as far as we have been able to ascertain [11].

If we have understood Paffen's expositions correctly, an Ökotop and a Soziotop are in a certain sense economic-geographic totalities. The former is a unit embodying very little cultural influence, the latter is a unit into which human activity has been integrated. This activity immediately affects the soil, the flora and the fauna, and often to a greater or lesser degree also the micro-climate. This new integration forms a Soziotop. The latter and the Ökotop, in so far as there is still an Ökotop in existence, together determine a Geotop.

In determining the spatial extension of an Ökotop and a Soziotop and that of groups of these units, Paffen starts from the integrating complex. He rightly opposes the use of the method of overlapping applied by many others, according to which larger and smaller topographic units are determined only from the result of the overlapping of the separate elements (not of the various integrations). Yet it should be borne in mind that in many cases very definite elements may be decisive of the significance of the soil. In the foregoing we have pointed this out repeatedly and in great detail. Here we only refer to the significance of the fine texture of the soil and of the smoothness of a territory for mechanical dry farming in the Great Plains, and of the different significance of the temperature and moisture of the atmosphere for the chorological differentiation of natural vegetation and cultivated crops.

The importance of an Ökotop and a Soziotop for the formation of geographic regions of vertical unity is determined by the significance of different groups of Ökotope — each of which consisting of a number of Ökotope of a particular type — for the chorological differentiation. This plays a part in Paffen's conceptions, it is true, but not a very striking part. Paffen discusses the distribution of similar Ökotope (die Lageverteilung gleichartiger Ökotope), but he emphasizes the mutual horizontal relations of dissimilar Ökotope (die gegenseitigen Lagebeziehungen der verschiedenartigen Ökotope) [12]. He indeed examines the way in which the uniformity and homogeneity of a micro-landscape (Kleinlandschaft) have been determined by the distributive pattern of the different groups of Ökotope. He ascertains how a particular group corresponds with a particular type of Ökotop, and in how far some of the groups are predominant. And then he speaks of the decreasing homogeneity, and of the more extensive ecological homogeneity (weitergespannter ökologischer Homogenität) of larger landscape units: The degree of homogeneity is in the first instance a factor of the complexity of a landscape and of its stage of integration (Der Homogenitätsgrad ist in erster Linie eine Function der Landschaftlichen Komplexität und Integrationsstufe) [13]. By the latter he means the degree to which the formation of a region has been accomplished. This is determined by ascending from Ökotope to a "Kleinlandschaft" via a process of combination; and in the same way "Kleinlandschaften" are combined into an "Einzellandschaft", and so on. But his conception of a landscape as a mosaic of Ökotope that differ ecologically [14] shows that he does not consider chorological differentiation as a differentiation of regions each with a maximum of homogeneity and uniformity. For an essential chorological differentiation is only possible if the regions show a maximal difference, and this stage is reached when every separate region possesses the highest degree of uniformity. The uniformity of a geographic region may be simple, but also complex.

This is why we cannot help feeling that Paffen considers the *essential* chorological differentiation to be only of secondary importance. In his expositions the horizontal interconnections occupy a central place, together with the structure of the vertical ecological process within the Ökotop *as such*.

Although the author may refrain from laying the stress on chorological differentiation, this does not detract from the importance for us to examine the significance of the Ökotop and the Soziotop for determining the differentiation of geographical regions of vertical unity. In the above we have pointed out the relativity of the extent of geographical regions, for this extent depends on the standards we apply to ascertain their chorological differentiation. Paffen, however, considers his Ökotop to be a reality whose spatial boundaries are a datum. An Ökotop is the smallest piece of ground that cannot be further divided, and forms a building-brick of a "Kleinlandschaft". According to Troll and Paffen [15] it is a limited and closed unit. Also the statement that Ökotope constitute a landscape in the same way as cells do an organism suggests that an Ökotop is a spatial datum which is independent of the investigator's standards. When, however, the homogeneity of a "Kleinlandschaft" is discussed, the investigator's judgment also begins to play its part. For this homogeneity depends on the degree to which some groups of Ökotope of a particular type are preponderant. The determination of this type is an activity of the human mind; the type is not a reality.

Hartshorne [16], Schmitthenner [17], Carol [18], and we ourselves [19], however, have always emphasized the fact that the earth surface is a continuum, and that geographic regions are never entirely independent units in whatever way they may have been determined. They depend on the standards, insights and aims of the thinking mind investigating the multiplicity of earthly reality. Geographical regions are units from a particular point of view, as we have explained above. Ökotope and "Landschaften", too, are units in a particular respect only in our opinion. They are units from the point of view of a habitat (Standort).

Schmitthenner, restricting himself to expressing an opinion on Schmithüsen's "Fliese" and Ökotop, says: The "Fliese", too, implies evaluation, supposition, and volitional aim (Wertung, Setzung, und gewolltes Ziel). With reference to the Ökotop he observes: "But this principle as the basis of finding a landscape is also abstract, and at bottom it is merely a method of spatial division on the basis of some factor or other" [20]. Although Paffen's Ökotop is less abstract than Schmithüsen's units, we are of the opinion that Schmitthenner's judgment is applicable here, too.

Plewe and Schmitthenner mention another point as well, however, when they observe that the knowledge of the ecological process of an Ökotop is certainly valuable, because an Ökotop contains a bundle of operations. But, they say, geography is not concerned with micro-regions. Geography is a macroscopic science.

Although we must admit that Paffen does not stop at these smallest topographic units, but composes landscapes of an ever increasing surface-extension, the investigation of these "Landschaftszellen" occupies a large place indeed. Just like Schmitthenner and Plewe we would emphasize the macroscopic character of geography. Geography wishes to know the world in its chorological diversity. It has to determine areas and regions. An area, the geographic environment of a human group, is not a micro-chora, but a macro-chora. Although the extent of a region depends on all kinds of factors and standards, we may say: The extent of a part of the world forming a human environment is a multiple of the extent of a part of the world which is the environment of a micro-biosphere.

Geography, say Plewe and Schmitthenner, "in the strict sense of the word, is a science for us, not a science as such (nicht an sich);

it is a macroscopic science. Every science tries to elucidate its material as such, but geography should explain our environment (Umwelt) to us" [21].

In his elaborate discussion of micro-geography Hartshorne arrives at the conclusion that the study of a very small region is only meaningful, if such a region is very important in itself, or if it is representative of a large region, and that the knowledge of such a micro-region yields knowledge of a macro-region. In connection with the latter he observes among other things: "If a geographer makes a detailed study of a single cotton farm in the Yazoo delta, he is not to forget that the geographic world is interested in the farm only in its significance to an understanding of the Yazoo delta, or even the Cotton Belt generally" [22].

We will conclude our detailed discussion of the Ökotop concept by asking: Is there any correlation of the chorological differentiation of vertical geographic regions and the chorological diversity of groups of Ökotope or Geotope? Let us consider a part of the world whose soil consists of young sea clay, and contains three adjoining economic-geographic regions, viz., an arable region, a dairy-farming region, and an industrial region. The question is then: Is there a chorological diversity of the vertical ecological integrations of groups of Geotope reflecting the chorological differentiation of these three economic-geographic regions? Does the differentiation of the vertical interrelation of the economic phenomena, and of other phenomena of these economic-geographic regions correspond with the chorological differentiation of the ecological complex of Geotope?

After our detailed exposition of the vertical unit of geographic totality, to which we would refer in this connection, we think we must say: There is only a very partial kind of correlation.

Particular cultural elements that are very important in the economic-geographic totality, such as the cooperation in dairy-factories, the common use of larger agricultural machines, particular industrial techniques, the size of the industry, the structure and function of cow-houses, stables and sheds, the type of factory buildings, will show hardly any relation to the structure and function of the Geotope involved. On the other hand vegetation, culti-

71

vated crops, the method of tilling the soil, the regulation of the level of the soil water, and milling will more or less be correlated with the properties of the Geotope constituting the geographic region in question. For the ascertainment of the particularity of the industry in that region the investigation of the Geotope will probably have little sense. There will practically be no correlation between the diversity of the structure and the function of the Geotope on the one hand and the question as to whether the industry is geographically bound or not, and if it is, in what way; whether there is an industry catering for the regional market, or an exporting industry. No more is there any correlation with the nature of the raw materials and the auxiliary materials supplied and used by the industry, or with the kinds of goods produced.

We have already observed that in a certain sense an Ökotop or a Geotop is an economic-geographic totality. This idea occurred to us because we noticed that these smallest topographical-geographic units were above all considered in connection with their significance to a habitat. But we had better call these units pedological-geographic unities. The soil is the nucleus to which all the other elements are related. This whole is then directed to the habitat. The latter procedure, however, has its drawbacks, and we do not think it is correct. Economic life should be the starting-point to which all the other elements are related. The way of life is determined by a combination of cultural and natural forces. Soil, hydrography, and climate are complexes with all kinds of possibilities within definite limits. They are not determining but conditional factors for the way of life. To this we should add that not all the existing possibilities are equally renumerative. To ascertain this fact the investigation of the ecological process within Ökotope and Soziotope may be very important. By the side of economic and social factors the constellation of the Ökotope has led the human group to the free, or to the more or less compulsory choice of its way of life. Also in the economic policy with respect to regions that are being brought into cultivation, or in planning the change and improvement of existing agrarian regions the examination of the ecological process of these small topographical units is important. This statement, however, leads us to the domain of economics. The theory of the habitat and that of the diversity of the habitat is part of economics and not of economic geography. In this connection Hartshorne's words are important: "The study of the 'Standorts' problem — the determination of principles governing location of units of production — not only requires more training in economics than in geography, but also requires a full concentration of interest on the problem for the sake of the problem itself, rather than for the sake of results; it is the economist who is interested in the problem, the geographer in the results" [23].

If the study of Ökotope is important for economic and agrarian investigation, it may be equally useful to economic geography. We again think of Hartshorne's discussion of the relation of economic geography to agricultural science. In it he gives the following demonstration, which appeals to us in connection with the ecological process of the soil: "The relation of annual variations of corn production to annual variations in rain fall is of great concern to the student of agriculture but is not of direct concern in geography, whereas the fact that the variations in rainfall in Nebraska have a greater effect on corn yields, than the same degree of variation in Pennsylvania, is of geographic concern" [24].

The investigation of the ecological process of Ökotope in Nebraska and Pennsylvania will probably yield valuable data to explain this differentiation. Such an investigation of Ökotope and Geotope would then immediately be directed to the differentiation of large regions as they are, not as they perhaps ought to be in view of private or public economic interest. This is not saying that geography and especially economic geography does not know of any norms. On the contrary, but its norms are no universal economic standards. We shall revert to this problem in a later context.

Geography is concerned with the existing world as it is. A geographer wants to know the essential chorological differentiation of the world in order to gain an insight into the unity of this diversity. This diversity is of a complicated nature, and if we wish to gain an insight into it, we must analyse this chorological differentiation into different unities of total differentiation, into unities of vertical geographical totality. On the ground of the chorological

73

extension of such unities of integrated differentiations we ascertain geographical regions.

The investigation of various groups of Ökotope may be significant to the determination of micro-physical-geographical regions. These small geographic regions are no data, but have been determined by the investigator in accordance with his standards of particular interrelated phenomena. These small regions are not an aim in themselves to geography, but must be the means to determine larger geographic regions in order to ascertain the chorological differentiation of the earth surface, chiefly from the point of view of the pedological-geographic totality.

In the last two chapters we have discussed the analysis of the chorologically differentiated complex and only paid attention to local vertical interrelations in more extensive geographical regions and in micro-regions. A geographical region and a micro-geograpical region, however, are not only determined by its vertical interrelations and unity. The horizontal interconnections and the relative unities formed on the basis of relative location are also important. This horizontal interconnection and its relation to the vertical integration must now be examined more closely.

CHAPTER V

UNITIES OF VERTICAL INTERRELATION AND HORIZONTAL INTERCONNECTION AS THE BASIS OF CHOROLOGICAL DIFFERENTIATION

The chorological diversity of the earth surface is a diversity of things in different localities. Things in one and the same locality are interrelated, form vertical interrelations or totalities. But things that vary chorologically and are vertically interrelated in one locality, are by no means all of them indigenous. Many material and immaterial things in a locality originate from other places, and these foreign things are incorporated with local things into a vertical interrelation. This also holds for man himself. Individual persons and groups emigrate and settle in another locality and in another country. It depends on the quality and the number of the emigrants in how far they will co-determine the vertical integration of the place and the region of settlement. The chorological diversity is first of all a chorological differentiation of these vertical local interrelations of indigenous and exotic things. These foreign things are evidence of the existence of interconnections between one place and other places. Such relations we shall call horizontal interconnections. However, we discover the results of this horizontal interconnection in the vertical interrelation of indigenous and foreign things in one locality sooner than the horizontal interconnection itself which is the cause of these results.

The things that are found in and on each other in one locality, and are interwoven with each other, possess an integration which is more or less a matter of course to us. How should it be otherwise? But things are different in the case of horizontal interconnection between one place and another place. To conquer distance movement is required; this distance may be great or small. The movements of things, of material and immaterial things, show differences in kind. Atmospheric movement is the effect of a difference in pressure, which in its turn depends on differences in the heating of the various areas and oceans. Hot and cold, dry and moist air are thus brought in or carried away, and this process is again strongly influenced by other circumstances, such as relief, the alternation of sea and land. Dust, sand and loess are also carried by the wind over great distances. Rivers, glaciers and seas carry silt, debris, and sand from one place to another and back again. Men carry material and immaterial things from one place to another by land and water and through the air. And lastly man himself moves away temporarily and also permanently. These motory phenomena vary greatly and depend on differences in material and mental culture. Modern cultural regions have more mutual horizontal interconnections and over much longer distances than primitive regions.

This horizontal chorological interconnection is very important. Things found in a particular locality are not isolated and do not exist only by themselves. Recall the Nile delta. The soil and the natural inundation of this region are also determined by the soil, the relief and the climate in Ethiopia and Eastern Sudan from where the Blue Nile and the White Nile carry the water with silt to the Nile delta.

Like the vertical interrelations, the horizontal interconnections have structure and function. On account of the motory phenomena within the horizontal interconnection their function is more emphatically in evidence here than the function of the vertical interrelation; although within this interrelation, too, there is a function of the differentiations for each other at every earthpoint. In the vertical interrelation, on the other hand, the structure is more marked. The structure of the horizontal interconnection is mostly very complicated and much less marked in a chorological respect.

We determine a geographical region first according to the chorological extension of the vertically interrelated differentiations. For this determination the absolute chorological extension of the ground or the soil is highly significant. Other earthly things display a certain amount of spread, which may vary in density. The chorological differentiation of these latter things may, or may not be interrelated with the differentiation of the soil.

The determination of a geographic region according to the homogeneity of its horizontal interconnections is more difficult, because

76

the horizontal extension of things is much less marked than that of the vertical interrelation.

With reference to Ullman's [1] opinion that geography is especially concerned with spatial interaction (horizontal interconnection) and that chorological differentiation is a sub-concept of this spatial interaction, Hartshorne [2] says that the horizontal interconnections also come under the chorological differentiation. In our opinion this seems to be correct. But the question may arise as to what constitutes the chorological differentiation of the horizontal interconnections.

In every locality there are differentiations of a complex of vertically interrelated things. Various things are carried from one locality to another and incorporated into the local vertical interrelation. The horizontal interconnection is a motory process going on between the vertical interrelations of two or more localities. The chorological diversity of the horizontal interconnections is manifest in the fact that the horizontal interconnection of the vertical interrelations of particular adjacent localities is stronger than that of these localities with other adjoining localities. In this way it is more or less possible for us to speak of geographical regions possessing a certain amount of *horizontal unity*. In every region the localities and the smaller parts of such a region are more closely connected with each other than with localities and small regions outside of that region and bordering on it. Bordering on this geographic region there are again others which in the same way, and to a greater or lesser degree, form horizontal unities. The chorological diversity then appears from the differentiation of the relative location of the localities, or of the relative location of the things found in these localities. Owing to their relative location with regard to one another the various localities and smaller parts of a geographic region possess a close horizontal interconnection, and in consequence of this they constitute a horizontal regional unity which is a relative whole. This geographic region is distinct from the surrounding regions, which on the basis of the relative locations of the localities of these regions also form horizontal unities: The horizontal regional unities are the result of the chorological differentiation of *unity in relative location*. A horizontal unity is a

77

whole only in a very relative sense, for there are also relations with localities outside of the region, although they are less close. A horizontal unity is, therefore, based on the evaluation of the importance of the horizontal interconnections. And further, this horizontal interconnection is mostly restricted to the integration of particular phenomena of the vertical complex of the localities and parts of the region concerned. With regard to the other phenomena of the vertical complex, it is often other localities that show a closer horizontal interconnection, and the region with the horizontal unity of these phenomena has a different extent and form. Just like the various regions of the vertical interrelation those of the horizontal interconnection will also overlap [3].

Is such a geographic region of relative horizontal unity a chora, determined by the chorological extension of its objects, as was the case with a geographical region of vertical unity?

A geographical region of vertical unity is determined by the uniform extension of the differentiations that form an integration. Several of these differentiations have an interrupted chorological extension, a certain amount of spread in varying degrees of closeness. All these differentiations, however, are found on the ground or partly in it. Independent of the question as to whether a particular chorological differentiation of the ground or the soil coalesces, or does not coalesce, with a particular chorological differentiation of the integration, the chorological extension of this vertical interrelation is determined by the absolute extension of the ground on or in which the differentiation of the vertical interrelation in question is to be found, and over which the latter is more or less densely spread. The chora formed by this vertical interrelation is a marked one.

The horizontal unity of region is based on motory processes between vertical integrations of different localities or of small regional parts. They occur *in* a chora. But here it is hardly possible to speak of the chorological extension of objects forming a chora.

The geographic regions with horizontal unity which we distinguish may often show little difference as to the "kind" of things and phenomena.

Let us consider a large agrarian region with a certain measure of uniformity of production and displaying vertical unity. This large region consists of a number of smaller regions, each with a certain amount of horizontal unity. Each of these small regions consists of a number of farms with a large village or a small country town. These farms and the village or the small town are interconnected by means of horizontal relations. The difference, the differentiation of these small regions with horizontal unity does not consist in a chorological differentiation of the forms of production in the country, nor of that of the large villages and the small country towns. The differentiation is based on a difference in horizontal interconnection, in which certain things of the localities of every small region are connected with each other more closely than with things in other localities situated outside of that small region and bordering on it.

In the chorological differentiation, the distinction between these geographic regions, each having relative horizontal unity, there is consequently much less question of a distinction within a particular kind of integration, as in the case of the vertical interrelations of juxtapositional arable and dairy-farming regions, horticultural, industrial and other regions of the economic-geographic totality. It is true, horizontal unity is founded on a particular kind of interconnected phenomena, e.g. on economic-geographic integration; but the distinction of the geographic regions of horizontal unity is not based on a difference within that "kind" of integration. The latter is often exactly the same. As we have explained, the chorological differentiation of regions with horizontal unity rests on the differentiation in relative location, or to put things more correctly, on a chorological differentiation of the unity of relative location.

In the example of a large agrarian region which we considered as a vertical uniform integration, in contradistinction to other large adjoining regions, we must observe that this region is looked upon here as a uniform rural producing region. The production and the vertical unity of the large villages and small towns are different from the rural production and its unity and have been ignored by us, because they are very small in comparison with those of the agrarian production of the country.

It will be clear that in a particular part of the world vertical and horizontal unity do not coalesce. Vertical regional unity is characterized by its uniformity. Horizontal unity of region is based on the interconnection of the parts of the region. This interconnection is above all based on a distinction, on a chorological differentiation of the vertical interrelation of the regional parts. The vertical interrelation of the farms is different from that of the large villages and the small towns. This is a clear case of chorological differentiation within an economic-geographic totality. It is precisely these differences that create the mutual horizontal connections between the farms and the village which give rise to a relative horizontal unity.

In accordance with a pronouncement made by Ullman, Hartshorne says that the integration of the things and phenomena of the various localities over a shorter distance is stronger than that of localities situated a long way from each other. Connected with this is the fact that the administration of every country has been organized in accordance with regional divisions [4].

Although Hartshorne does not underrate "long-range movements" in modern countries, we must enter further into the significance of these horizontal long-range connections. The localities and areas between which these horizontal interconnections are found, are often parts of different countries or states.

Let us consider the Dutch horticultural region of Westland and its horizontal interconnections with the Ruhr region. The fact that the latter region is one of the most important buyers of the horticultural products of Westland is perhaps more important for this horticultural region than any other horizontal short-range connection within Westland itself. The relations between Westland and the Ruhr region are unilateral. The Ruhr region is more important for Westland than Westland is for this industrial region. The relation is exclusively based on the exportation and the importation of particular horticultural products. So it is both a unilateral and a simple horizontal relation. But the effect of this relation has a great influence on the whole of the vertical economic interrelation

80

in Westland. Of course it is true that Westland is a part of The Netherlands, and the Ruhr region is a part of the German Federal Republic, and that these two countries have a large mutual import and export trade. But the part of the German export that Westland gets in return bears no proportion to the part of the total production of Westland, received by the Ruhr region.

Horizontal long-range connections of a locality, or of a region with other localities and regions may also be extremely many-sided and very comprehensive. The economic and the technical horizontal interconnections of the Ruhr region with other regions are world-wide. Its import of raw materials and certain auxiliary materials, and goods for immediate consumption, compares with its export of coal, capital goods, durable consumption goods, finished goods of the most divergent kinds, and the loan of technicians. This export of material and also of immaterial things via multi-lateral horizontal connections is regional, national, and inter-national.

Primitive countries, on the other hand, have few or hardly any long-range relations, except in those cases in which such areas function as conquered countries and export particular raw materials with the aid of the capital and the technique provided by modern countries.

When we call a region a horizontal unity, we refer to the *internal* horizontal interconnection. The horizontal interconnection with localities and regions outside of it we will call *external* horizontal interconnection. As a result the horizontal unity based on the internal horizontal interconnection is restricted. It constitutes a relative whole. Especially in modern countries this internal horizontal unity is restricted. In primitive countries this unity, this whole, is often more pronounced.

So the internal horizontal unity is generally characterized by a close mutual interconnection of localities and parts within this geographic region, which interconnection is closer than that of the localities of this region with localities outside of it and bordering on it. If this were not so, these localities would also be added to this geographic region. As has been observed in an earlier context, this internal horizontal unity is restricted to the horizontal inter-

81

connection of particular phenomena, and depends on all kinds of standards applied by the investigator.

We have already pointed out in the above (Chapter III) that some particular interrelations, which we have called vertical interrelations, are really horizontal integrations. In a village, e.g., there are a few shops and schools, a church, and a cultural centre. These material and immaterial things are at the disposal of the inhabitants, and thus the latter are more or less related with them. This integration we designate as a vertical interrelation, because in thought we identify the separate localities of shop-buildings, schools, of the church, etc., with the place occupied by the houses of the inhabitants. In studying this area in which the village occupies only a very small part of the area, we think it is permissible to ignore the distances between the shops, schools, etc., and the houses of the inhabitants, and to speak of vertical interrelations. In reality they are horizontal interconnections at a very short-range. The same thing holds for a farm. Its fields and pastures form a small horizontal unity with the farmhouse and the trade building. The relative location of the cowhouses and stables, the barns, and the smaller buildings is also evidence of a horizontal interconnection. This is even more emphatically true of the various departments of a factory. In our study of an area, however, and of the horizontal interconnections of the farms with a village, we may ignore the short-range horizontal interconnection within every farm, and consider these farms as productive units, as vertical interrelations. These farms are horizontally interconnected with the vertical and the horizontal integrations of the village.

The vertical and the horizontal integrations influence each other strongly, as has already been indicated by the significance of the horizontal motory process for the vertical interrelation of exotic and indigenous things in a locality. We may even say that the horizontal interconnections are strong co-determinants of the chorological differentiation of the vertical interrelations: The demand for particular goods in certain regions has a great influence on the character of the production in another region which is horizontally interconnected with the former regions. This horizontal integration (interconnection), therefore, greatly influences the character

82

of that region as a chorological differentiant, by which that region is distinguished as a vertical unity from the vertical unity of other regions.

The influence of the horizontal interconnection is also very important for a certain degree of uniformity of particular vertical interrelations of the various parts of a country, especially those of a state. The similarity according to particular characteristics follows from the fact that they are parts of a comparative whole [5]. Thus, e.g., a man who has spent some time in Sauerland (South Westphalia) can say: "I have been in Western Germany". He can tell us something about German conditions, institutions, and circumstances of a cultural, a political, and of an economic character, even though he has only been in South Westphalia. In a certain respect Sauerland as a part of Western Germany reflects the general characteristics of Western Germany as a whole. The similarity and the uniform chorological extension of certain vertical interrelations in this case rests on the effect of the horizontal interconnection of the unity as a whole. We might ask: Where is then the chorological differentiation of Western Germany into different regions of which Sauerland is one? This chorological differentiation is certainly there. For we do not say that Sauerland is like the other parts of Western Germany in every respect. There is a great deal of chorological differentiation, but at the same time there is also similarity in certain respects. We have put this similarity in the foreground ignoring many differentiations. Chorological differentiation does not mean that regions are different in all their characteristics and properties. The characteristics that Sauerland has in common with other regions of Germany, however, also form a differentiant. These characteristics will be significant for distinguishing Germany as a chorological differentiant from other countries. This chorological differentiation is based on more *generally* distinctive characteristics. This means that larger countries can be divided into smaller regions that may be called special chorological differentiations within a more general differentiation. And conversely: Different regions, considered to be chorological differentiants, are combined into a larger country. These regions are distinct from each other, but they share the more general characteristics

83

of the more general chorological differentiant, the country. There is a certain hierarchy within the chorological differentiation. In Chapter VII we shall elaborate this point.

So the horizontal unity influences the uniform chorological extension of particular vertical interrelations, but in other cases we can speak of the uniform extension of the *kind* of horizontal interconnections resulting from the uniform chorological extension of vertical interrelations. In the example given above of a large agrarian region (p. 79.) we could say that this region consists of a number of small regions, each of which forms a horizontal unity on the ground of the horizontal interconnection of its farms with a large village or a small country town. The structure of this horizontal unity is the same in all these small regions, and has a uniform extension [6]. The chorological differentiation is manifest in the diversity of the function of the horizontal unities, which is founded on a differentiation of their relative locations. The structure of the horizontal interconnections, however, is the same in the small regions. It is the result of the uniform chorological extension of groups of farms, each with a large village or a small town. These farms and country places form two groups of vertical interrelations. The chorological extension of the latter group is small in comparison with the surface extension of the farms (homesteads with their landed estates). Because of the magnitude of the agrarian production, which possesses a certain measure of uniformity, and in connection with its surface extension, we can speak of a large agrarian geographic region with vertical unity.

Is this large agrarian region also a horizontal unity? As we have explained, the structure of the horizontal interconnections in all the small regions of this large one is the same. But there is more needed for horizontal unity, viz., a closer interconnection of the localities and the parts of a region with each other than with the adjoining localities and areas outside of this region. A horizontal unity is a relative whole, a functional unity. The different small regions of the large agrarian region are horizontal unities. A group of farms and a small country town possess close horizontal interconnections owing to relative location, and form a horizontal unity. The various small regions of the large agrarian region are distinguished by their different relative locations. This large region, therefore, displays a chorological differentiation of horizontal unities based on a differentiation of relative location. But on the ground of the data which we have put forward up to now, this large agrarian region is not a horizontal unity yet. It merely displays the uniform extension of the structure of the horizontal interconnection. The large region is the sum total of horizontal unities, of horizontal small regions, but it is not a functional whole of horizontal interconnections.

If, however, we consider other horizontal interconnections that have not yet been mentioned, the picture changes. Let us suppose that in the large agrarian region there are two large towns which have only partly the character of a country town. If we include these towns in our investigation, it will appear that the various small regions have horizontal interconnections with these two large towns. The various farms of every small region are mostly connected with one of these large towns via a village or a small country town with which this group of farms forms a small region of horizontal unity. Consequently, via the interconnection with either of the two large towns the small geographic regions are included into two larger regions. Each of these two regions of the whole agrarian region forms a horizontal unity. This unity, however, is characterized by a less close horizontal interconnection than the horizontal interconnection within the unity of each small region. The relative horizontal unity of these two larger regions is, therefore, chiefly formed by the horizontal interconnection of the large villages and small rural towns with the two large towns. But these interconnections are indirectly based on the relations of the farms with the villages and small country towns.

The large agrarian region consists of a great number of small regions, each having horizontal unity. It also embraces two larger regions, each of which forms a relative horizontal unity whose unity and interconnection are not so close, however. If the large agrarian region itself is a part of a state, and this state has a strong influence on economic-social life, this large agrarian region itself is not an economic-geographic horizontal unity. It is not a whole which controls and directs its parts. It is the sum total of two separate horizontal regions that are very much alike. But the large region is indeed a vertical unity, because it has a uniform chorological extension of an agrarian-geographic interrelation.

The small regions, and also the two larger regions of the large agrarian region are horizontal unities, but no vertical unities. They are parts of a vertical unity, of the large agrarian region. For we speak of a vertical unity if a region can be distinguished from the vertical integration of the adjoining regions by its vertical inter-relation. The above-mentioned small regions and the two larger ones have the same kind of vertical interrelation. Precisely on account of the uniform chorological extension of this vertical agrarian interrelation, the large agrarian region as a whole is a vertical unity which is distinct from the vertical interrelation of the adjoining large regions. Within the large agricultural region there is no question of a chorological differentiation of vertical geographic unities. There is indeed a chorological differentiation of the country side (farms) and villages and towns, in which, however, the surface extent of the chorai of the farms (homesteads and estates) far exceeds the surface extent of the villages and towns.

The horizontal unity of the small regions is stronger than that of the two larger regions. The two larger towns only partly have the character of a country town. These towns also have an industry whose products are exported to various other regions. These large towns have many external horizontal connections with other regions so that there is no question of a closed horizontal unity. The small regions of this large agrarian region have a closer hori-zontal unity. But these regions are no closed and independent unities either. Via a large village or a small country town there are again all kinds of relations with one of the large towns, and some of these small regions have horizontal interconnections with both large towns. But not only this: The large agrarian region and its regional parts have external horizontal interconnections with localities and regions outside of them, via the exportation of agrarian products and the importation of capital goods and consumers' goods. The regions we have formed are only unities in certain respects.

Within a state and within the mutual interconnections between states there are similar integrations to those we have discussed in the example of a large agrarian region. Let us, e.g., consider the Netherlands as a relative whole, as a horizontal unity consisting of a number of geographic regions that are the component parts of the Netherlands. In certain respects these regions are vertical unities. Every region is a uniform productive region, either a simple or a compound one. These vertical geographic regions are mutually connected within the Netherlands by horizontal interconnections, and provide for each other for a great part. In addition to these internal horizontal interconnections within the Netherlands many regions have external horizontal interconnections with regions of other states. Part of the production of the Dutch regions is exported, and these regions receive goods from abroad in return. These external connections of the regions of the states are very important. Some regions produce more for abroad than for the other parts of the state. The external horizontal interconnections of these regions of the different states, however, are not direct, but exist via the states involved as wholes. The state lays down the rules of imports and exports for all its regions, for the whole country. It decides upon the quantity of particular goods that in certain cases will and may be imported or exported.

The territory of the state is a unity of political, cultural and of particular economic phenomena. For rules, legal provisions and instructions create a certain amount of uniformity in the economic life of the regions in the territory of the state. These situations and circumstances form vertical interrelations displaying a certain degree of similarity in every locality and in every part of the state, because they all belong to the territory of that state. Owing to this the state also has the characteristics of a vertical geographic unity. The state as a horizontal unity is a whole consisting of regions, which are both formed and controlled by it. These regions differ in vertical unity, and are horizontally interconnected within the whole of the state. But the whole controls the parts (the regions) to such an extent that the parts resemble each other in certain *other* respects, as has been explained in an earlier context by means of the example of Sauerland, which reflects particular characteristics of Western Germany as a whole.

One is perhaps inclined to say that this vertical unity, this uniform chorological extension of vertical integrations (interrelations) of the state, is restricted. Only particular integrations of the entire vertical complex are uniform.

The territory of the state is not a total chorological differentiant, no more than any other geographic region. In the areas on both sides of the frontier between two states there is often little difference in soil, in climate, and in hydrography. Cultivated crops and forms of production, too, may show little difference in these areas. But there is also often a strong differentiation in various phenomena of these states. We are referring to the different prices of the crops and the products, to the difference in the value of money, and the diversity in the economic policy of the states, which latter phenomenon appears from the difference in the regulations and legal provisions in the social-economic and the financial spheres. These differences often have a great influence on the way of life, and may give rise to a difference in the use of the soil.

With Hettner and Hartshorne we are of opinion that geography is the science of the chorological differentiation of the phenomena of nature and of those cultural phenomena that are connected with natural phenomena. But as to cultural phenomena, it does not mean that only those phenomena are concerned which are influenced by nature. It also means that those phenomena are meant which exert their influence on nature. Well, the chorological differentiation of the earth surface into states is often very important for the chorological differentiation of other phenomena, also for the phenomena of the nature of the earth surface.

The differentiation of the world into states has great geographic significance. For any chorological differentiation of the earth surface is geographically important, if it results in geographic regions that are significant to their human inhabitants on account of structure and function. Well then, the political differentiation forms countries with distinct political, economic, financial, and cultural characteristics. The differences in these important characteristics are of great significance to these countries as distinct dwelling-places of human groups. For this reason the state is an important geographic region, and the political differentiation is a chorological differentiation of great importance.

The various adjoining states intensively cooperating in the political, the economic, and the cultural spheres, form a larger horizontal unity with a less close integration than that of the horizontal unity of each of the states themselves. The external horizontal interconnections between the states, and between the regions of the states, form as it were the internal horizontal interconnection of this larger and looser horizontal unity. We are referring to the Benelux for instance. The modern world has many such larger and more loosely integrated wholes in the economic, the military, and the political spheres. In this context we are also referring to the NATO, the E.E.C. (European Economic Community), the Warsow Pact and to other organizations [7]. Such a large, but very relative horizontal unity may enter into relations with another large unity. In the case of the horizontal interconnections between the latter large unities we must pay attention to the uniformity of each separate unity or whole; even though this unity is very much restricted. The interconnections, both the positive and the negative ones, between these large loose wholes, however, require a certain degree of uniformity with regard to particular things within each of these large wholes. With respect to these things the states, constituting that whole, display a certain degree of similarity of particular vertical interrelations. In this sense this loosely constructed whole not only forms a limited horizontal unity but also a limited vertical unity. In other words it forms a chorological differentiant, a vertical geographic region, and because of the mutual relative locations of the component parts (the separate states) it is a horizontal unity. The integration is very much restricted, but the chorological extension, the region, is very large. We must bear in mind, however, that there is only question of vertical and horizontal unity of geographic region if these large loose wholes consist of countries that border on each other and form one uninterrupted region. Very often this is not the case, although the horizontal interconnection is mostly not less intensive. In such cases there is no question of one region, but of more regions, which together form a horizontal unity with an interrupted chorological extension.

We have amply discussed various horizontal and vertical integrations, and we think we are justified in drawing the following conclusion: The unities of vertical and horizontal integration do not coalesce in many respects; the chorological extension, the geographic region of each of the two unities is often different, the regions overlap. The unity, either vertical or horizontal, is generally restricted to one single integration of phenomena. Even within this single integration this unity is limited to a few phenomena. When we consider another integration in that region, the chorological extension of the unity of that integration is mostly different, and the latter overlaps the region of the former integration.

Agrarian regions, industrial regions, and states are only regions in certain respects. The state as a country comprises a complex of chorological differentiations displaying a close integration. But even the state is not a chorological unity of all the interrelated natural, cultural, economic, and political differentiations. The total complex of terrestrial things and phenomena cannot be conceived as a differentiation of either vertical or horizontal chorological unities, because chorai are no organisms like the individuals of the biotic world.

When discussing the dimensions of a region in Chapter II we pointed out the significance of the two dimensions determining the extension of the surface. From the standpoint of geography these two dimensions are the most important. The third dimension is, as it were, a further determination of the other two that determine the surface. We also pointed out the significance of geographic longitude and geographic latitude. These two with the indication of altitude determine absolute geographic location. This location in its turn determines vertical and horizontal integration.

The vertical integration of things in one and the same locality rests on the fact that these things have the same absolute location. This does not mean, of course, that the nature of these things and their interrelation in one locality are determined by their having

90

the same absolute location. Technical and spiritual culture and the economic order determine whether and how man and nature in one locality are interrelated. But the fact that they have the same absolute location is the basis and the pre-requisite of the vertical interrelation of things that are interwoven with each other in one locality.

Different localities have different absolute locations, and as a result these localities have mutual relative locations. The horizontal interconnection of things in different localities is essentially based on this relative location. Here, too, we must point out that the mere fact of relative location does not automatically occasion a particular horizontal interconnection. The character of things in different localities and the distance between them are of decisive importance. We are especially referring to the horizontal interconnection of human things. In connection with the mutual supply with goods and services many factors are important, such as location on navigable rivers, railways and motor roads; location on deep waterways, the connection with the oceans, and location with respect to the great shipping routes and the air routes. These natural and cultural things are only significant, and have a different significance in connection with the character and the level of technique, the spiritual culture, the economic order of a locality, and whether the economic order is local or very much interlocal. In the case of natural things the issue is among other things the relative location of localities with respect to prevailing winds, ocean currents, and rivers carrying heat or cold, drought or moisture, and component elements of the soil to and from a locality.

The local vertical interrelations are subject to all kinds of modifications on account of these horizontal interconnections. Foreign things are incorporated into indigenous vertical interrelations and then carried away again by horizontal interconnections in processes of horizontal movement.

Hettner speaks of the "spatial interconnection of juxtapositional things and of the relations between different terrestrial localities and their spatial interconnection mostly mediated by motory processes" [8]. Among other things he mentions the importance of the variation of high and low for the movement of the water and

91

the atmosphere. In our opinion it is especially the *differences* between the vertical interrelations of the various localities that bring about the process of the movement of the horizontal interconnections. So the chorological *differentiation* of the vertical interrelations is the operative factor of the horizontal interconnection.

Vertical and horizontal integration, however, is not identical with vertical and horizontal unity, and this is why the question arises: What about the significance of location with respect to these regional unities?

Vertical unity is characterized by the uniform chorological extension of vertical interrelations. It is possible to indicate a region by determining its absolute location within limits. On the basis of these limits the regions can be distinguished from each other, for one of the two determinations, viz., longitude or latitude, is always different in two or more regions. This differentiation, however, is of little importance: there may be great differentiation of particular phenomena over a small distance, so that the differentiation in absolute location (longitude and latitude) is small. There may be little differentiation and great uniformity in certain phenomena over a long distance in which, consequently, the differentiation in absolute location is considerable.

As has already been observed, the equality of absolute location of things is a pre-requisite of vertical interrelation, but this location determines the nature and the interrelation of things only to a small degree. No doubt its absolute location with respect to geographic latitude and altitude is important for the climate of a locality, especially for its temperature. But there are many other factors that determine the climate of a locality, such as its relative location manifest in the distribution of land and water, in the east or the west side of a continent, or of the interior. Another important factor is relief. If the equality of absolute location is a pre-requisite of the vertical interrelation of things and phenomena, it is only of limited significance to the nature of things, and it is even less important for the uniform chorological extension of the differentiation of things and their integration. It is possible to imagine an area with a uniform climate and broadly speaking, with uniform geographic latitude. Partly this uniform latitude is decisive of the character of that climate. The upper soil, too, which is closely interrelated with the climate, displays a certain degree of uniformity. But the structure of the sub-soil, the mineral deposits, and a river running through this area have little or nothing to do with that geographic latitude. Economic life, and cultural goods, may display great chorological differentiation in this area. Man makes things unequal that may have been equal originally, and things which were different at first are purposely made equal by man. As has already been stated before, many things, above all the soil, have several possibilities. One and the same soil possesses different possibilities for human life, and different soils have a common possibility within their various possibilities for human existence. The uniform chorological extension in vertical unities of economic-geographic or cultural-geographic, or politico-geographic totality shows little connection with equality or inequality of absolute location of things.

If this absolute location is of very restricted significance, relative location is of greater moment for the vertical unity. The horizontal processes of movement introduce foreign things into a region where they are taken up and assimilated into the indigenous vertical interrelations.

The real significance of relative location is manifest in horizontal unity. For we speak of horizontal unity of region, if owing to their relative locations the localities of such a region are more closely connected with each other than with adjoining localities outside of this region.

Considering these data in connection with the chorological differentiation, we may state the following:

Owing to many forms of horizontal interconnection, relative location partly determines the nature of the vertical interrelations and vertical unities, and thus relative location partly determines the *chorological differentiation* into vertical unities.

Relative location combines similar and especially dissimilar vertical interrelations of different localities into a horizontal unity of region, and also brings about the horizontal interconnections of different regions. On account of the diversity of unity in relative location we speak of a chorological differentiation of the earth surface into horizontal regional unities.

Relative location, therefore, is very important for the chorological differentiation of vertical unities of region, for the chorological differentiation of horizontal unities of region, and for the interconnection of the regions of the world. The latter combines the chorological differentiations (the regions) of the world into a unity. Owing to the horizontal interconnections of the different regions we can speak of the structure (Gliederung) of the earth, as Hettner, and before him Ritter, had established [9]. It goes without saying that, as far as the interconnections between man and nature are concerned, these horizontal interconnections do not arise automatically, but are widely different in character and in intensity on earth, in accordance with human knowledge and skill as well as with human needs and the possibilities of the relation between man and nature.

The earth surface, the world, is a whole. It consists of parts which, in their turn, form relatively smaller wholes, which are again composed of smaller parts. Owing to the complexity of the various vertical and horizontal integrations the earth consists of a plurality of comparative wholes and their parts, which do not coalesce chorologically but overlap each other in many ways.

To the chorological differentiation of the world the vertical and the horizontal integrations are both essential. As we have explained in an earlier context, vertical integration and unity are of primary importance for the chorological differentiation. The different chorai are formed by the vertical unity in connection with the chorological extension of the objects. The ground (soil) in its absolute chorological extension is the pre-requisite of the chorological extension of the interrelated objects independent of the question as to whether or not the soil region determines the geographic region of the vertical interrelation. There is, however, another reason why the chorological differentiation in the vertical unity is most marked. Geography is concerned with the totality of the differentiations, and this totality of the phenomena is stronger in a vertical than in a horizontal unity. It is true, horizontal interconnection is also intrinsically totalitarian, because it is an inte-

94

gration of similar and dissimilar vertical *interrelations*. But this horizontal interconnection is often restricted to the interconnection of a few phenomena of the vertical interrelations. However, the vertical interrelation of a region as a totality mostly undergoes and assimilates the influence of a particular phenomenon that affects it via the horizontal interconnection with the vertical interrelation of another region.

Paffen emphasizes horizontal interconnection, and especially the interconnection of Ökotope that differ. He speaks of the chorological distribution (Lageverteilung) of similar Ökotope, and the mutual relations of place of different Ökotope (die gegenseitigen Lagebeziehungen der verschiedenartigen Ökotope). According to him the ecological structure of action (ökologischer Wirkungsgefüge) existing between the Ökotope of a micro-landscape (Kleinlandschaft) is based especially on the difference between the component Ökotope [10]. Indeed, the horizontal interconnection between different vertical interrelations is of decisive significance to their horizontal unity. But especially in the cultural phenomena there is also a strong interconnection between the similar parts of a region. This similarity of parts is based on the horizontal interconnection within the whole [11]. This whole and its parts, however, are only uniform in certain respects.

In modern economic regions, in which the external horizontal interconnections play an important rôle, it is precisely the vertical unity of region that is of great significance. A region as a vertical unity enters into relations with the vertical unity of other regions via the external horizontal interconnections. In the mutual connections of the states the vertical unity of a state also comes strongly to the fore. This is not saying that the internal horizontal unity of a country or a state is not very important, but this internal unity recedes a little into the background in this connection, and is broken through by the external horizontal interconnections.

Troll and Paffen look upon geographic regions, especially "Kleinlandschaften", as total unities. In chapters III and IV we have explained in detail that vertical unities of geographic region have been extracted from reality. Our inquiry into the horizontal

95

unity of region leads to the same conclusion. The external horizontal interconnections break through the internal horizontal interconnections. The horizontal unity of a region, which is based on the internal horizontal interconnection, has only been obtained by evaluating the significance of the various horizontal interconnections, as we have discussed in great detail. This internal horizontal unity is of a very relative nature and is only valid for a given integration, a particular unity of totality. This unity of totality is an abstraction from the complex of which it is a component part.

Hartshorne says: "The area itself is only an intellectual framework of phenomena, an abstract concept which does not exist in reality. The conditions are reality, the regions are intellectual conceptions" [12].

Vertical and horizontal unities of region are abstractions in a certain sense. But it is a problem apart whether we must go as far as Hartshorne, who conceives of them as pure things of reason. These geographic regions can be ascertained in reality. But they can only exist within the reality of the total complex of things and phenomena that are found in vertical and horizontal integrations.

There are no unities of chorological differentiation relating to the total complex, although chorological unities of differentiation of a limited integration can indeed be pointed out. We must admit, however, that such unities can only be ascertained by using particular *standards*. These geographic regions are no individual entities. They have been determined by the investigator in accordance with qualitative and quantitative standards of differentiation. Quality is primary, for it concerns the nature of the characteristics of the phenomena that differ chorologically. Next, the investigator has to decide what quantity entitles him to speak of a differentiation. Besides, it is often difficult to separate quality from quantity. In the case of a certain quantity of moisture we speak of a dry region, and when this quantity is larger, we speak of a moist region. Geographic regions are *determined* and not merely *given* in reality. But they are not pure things of reason either [13]. Schmitthenner says: "As such a landscape or a geographic region is non-existent. The only given datum is the very variable plurality of the continuum of the earth surface" [14].

To gain an insight into this complex continuum of vertical and horizontal integrations, analysis is necessary. This analysis shows us limited unities of geographic region, which regions are unities of limited integration. This integration is a part of reality, and only exists as a part of a complex, and not separately. In this sense it is an abstraction. The region of this integration, however, can be pointed out in the world. But this region as a vertical unity does not exist separately, because the integration is interlaced with other integrations of the vertical complex. Moreover, although the region as a vertical unity can be determined, it does not exist independently in its horizontal unity either. It is a part of the world as a whole, and cannot exist outside of this whole. It is insolubly bound up with the continuum of the earth surface. In this sense the region is also an abstraction.

Hartshorne [15], and Carol [16] speak of formal and functional unities of region. Formal unity is concerned with the uniformity, the structure of a region, corresponding to the structure of our unity of vertical interrelation. Functional unity corresponds to our functional interconnection of horizontal unity.

But we prefer the concepts vertical and horizontal integration and unity. We would submit that these concepts do better justice to the chorological element and to geographic location. As to the structure and the function of the regions, we must repeat what has been observed in an earlier context: The vertical integration (interrelation) has structure and function, although the former is more pronounced than the latter. The structure or architecture is at once clear. As to the function: At every point on earth the differentiations have a function for each other within an interrelation, and the interrelation as a totality controls and directs the function of the differentiations constituting the interrelation. Vertical unity of region is the uniform chorological extension of a vertical interrelation. The structure of the vertical unity of region is equal to the structure of the interrelation at some point in the region. The function of the vertical unity of region is also equal to the function of the interrelation at some point in the region.

The structure and the function of the vertical unity are influenced by the function of the external horizontal interconnections, because many things from abroad are imported via the horizontal process of movement and taken up by the local vertical interrelations.

Horizontal integration (interconnection) and horizontal unity are also characterized by structure and function. This structure reveals the architecture of the horizontal interconnections within a horizontal unity of region, and of the architecture of the horizontal interconnections of this region with localities and regions outside of it. The function of the internal horizontal interconnections and unity is formed by the process of movement within the horizontal unity of region. The function of the external horizontal interconnections is formed by the process of movement resulting from the horizontal interconnections of this region, and of localities within this region, with localities and regions outside of it. The function of the horizontal interconnections and their unity are more pronounced than the structure. The structure and the function together with the unity of the internal horizontal interconnections are intensively controlled by the structure of the vertical interrelations within the horizontal unity of region. The structure and the function of the external horizontal interconnections are determined by the differentiation of the structure of the different regions of vertical unity. For the *differences* of the vertical unity of the regions are the cause of the process of movement of the external horizontal interconnections, although in accordance with what we are explaining, and have explained before, the vertical unity of region in its structure and function is influenced by the function of the external horizontal interconnections. For the character and the structure of a producing region are partly determined by the demand for particular goods required by other regions. The external horizontal interconnections of these regions with this producing region partly determine the vertical unity of the latter region.

CHOROLOGICAL DIFFERENTIATION AND INTERCONNECTION VERSUS HISTORICAL CHANGE AND DEVELOPMENT

As has been pointed out in the Introduction to this study, Hettner places the geographical aspect by the side of the historical aspect and opposes the one to the other. He says: "Geography is the science of the spatial arrangement of things on the surface of the earth. The historical sciences receive their unity from the standpoint of the temporal process of things (durch den Gesichtspunkt des zeitlichen Ablaufes der Dinge) [1].

For the "spatial arrangement" of things on the surface of the earth two circumstances are important: "The one is . . . the differentiation from locality to locality by the side of the spatial interconnection of juxtapositional things. No phenomenon of the earth surface can be conceived of as something in itself, it is always intelligible only if we consider its relative location with respect to other places on earth. The second circumstance is the causal interrelation of the different natural kingdoms and their various phenomena united in one terrestrial locality" [2]. In another passage Hettner again emphasizes the principle of chorological differentiation: "Geography is the science of the earth surface according to its local differences (örtlichen Unterschieden), of the parts of the world, countries, landscapes and localities" [3].

With this Hettner compares the historical diversity or differentiation of things and their phenomena at different times, and the interconnection of things at different periods of time revealed in their development. If we understand him correctly, the interrelation of dissimilar things and their phenomena in one locality and at a given time is a circumstance which, according to Hettner, is the same for geography and for history [4].

The gist of Hettner's thought is that the diversity from place to place, and the interconnections between the various places are geographic principles. The diversity of different times and the interconnections between the different periods are historical principles *.

Ritter had already expressed this thought before that time, although less sharply: "The geographical sciences have preferably to do with the spaces of the earth surface is so far as they are terrestrially filled (to whatever natural kingdom they may belong, and irrespective of their forms); consequently with the descriptions and the circumstances of the coordination of the localities as such, in their most particular appearance as well as in their most general aspects. In this respect they are distinct from the historical sciences, which have to disclose, to investigate and to ascertain the way in which events happen one after another, or the order of succession and the development of individual things and their totality from within, and in an outward direction" [5].

In his penetrating study on Carl Ritter, Van Paassen has shown that Ritter has founded the chorological principle in his works, together with other important principles, which we shall discuss later on. This chorological principle is implied in the local interrelation of a totality of distinct things and phenomena and in the interconnection of these things and phenomena of different localities [6].

We have brought these thoughts, advanced by Ritter, to the fore, together with Van Paassen's observations, because Schmitthenner argues that Ritter classifies geography with the historical sciences [7].

Hettner places geography and history side by side and opposes the one to the other, as we have already observed. He opposes them in order to distinguish the two sciences, and he places them side by side in order to point out their relationship and to distinguish them from the systematic experimental sciences. The systematic sciences "relegate temporal and local events to the background and find their unity in the similarity or the affinity of the individual things with the objects with which they are concerned (finden ihre

---

* We speak of the *interrelation* of different phenomena at one point of time and of the historical *interconnection* between phenomena of different points of time in the past.

Einheit in der dinglichen Gleichartigkeit oder Verwandtschaft der Gegenstände mit denen sie sich beschäftigen)". For geography and history "the relations between the kind of things of their fields of study (die dinglichen Beziehungen ihrer Objekte) are of secondary importance. In the views of these sciences a number of things are combined that belong to quite different systems" . . . [8].

This difference in particular between geography and the systematic sciences had already been pointed out by Ritter. Van Paassen has clearly established this fact. He says: Ritter is interested in "the spatial cooperation of the system of nature as it appears to us in its local totality"; he is interested in the combination of the terrestrial datum. He is not concerned with each of the phenomena apart in its own causal complex, but with these phenomena in their combined diversity and mutual local relations, in their concrete existence. Ritter has shown geography the difficult road of the concrete spatial or individualizing way of approach. This is what Van Paassen says [9].

Hettner's basic thoughts about the geographic aspect have been thoroughly investigated and elaborated by Hartshorne. Hartshorne's general view can best be rendered by means of a quotation: "In sum, then, geography, like history, is to be distinguished from other branches of science not in terms of objects or phenomena studied, but rather in terms of fundamental functions. If the fundamental functions of the systematic sciences can be described as the analysis and synthesis of particular kinds of phenomena, that of the chorological and historical sciences might be described as the analysis and synthesis of the actual integration of phenomena in sections of space and time. — Both history and geography might be described as naive sciences, examining reality from a naive point of view, looking at things as they are actually arranged and related, in contrast to the more sophisticated but artificial procedure of the systematic sciences which take phenomena of particular kinds out of their real settings" [10].

And as to the difference between geography and history, Hartshorne says among other things: "We might say that both history and geography are attempts at descriptive integration, but that in history the integrating factor is time — the association of phenomena taking place at approximately the same place but related to each other in the sense of time — whereas in geography the integrating factor is space — the association of phenomena at approximately the same time, but related to each other in spatial terms, i.e., in terms of relative location" [11].

When in what follows we want to try to define the geographical aspect more exactly with reference to these pronouncements, made by Hettner and Hartshorne, and on the basis of our expositions in the preceding chapters, we shall every time try to oppose a historical concept as a counter-pole to a particular geographical concept.

Beforehand we must say that we are unable to decide whether these historical concepts are significant or not, as we are not qualified for such a judgment in the domain of historical science.

In spite of this, our attempt to find the counter-pole to every geographical concept in the science of history is an experiment which is necessary for the following reasons:

The conception of geography as a chorological science, and in particular as the science of the chorological differentiation of earthly reality, is in a certain sense a postulate to us. Broadly speaking geography is clear to us from this point of view as a science. This is not saying that there is not any question left unanswered. On the contrary. But we are convinced that with this view we are on the right road. If, however, we accept Hettner's and Hartshorne's basic idea — that earthly reality in its chorological differentiation and interconnection is the opposite of earthly reality in its historical diversity and interconnection (the course of history) — then, in our opinion, the geographical concepts that can be inferred from the first term of the comparison and contrast will have to correspond with the historical concepts that can be inferred from the second term of the comparison and contrast. If this is not the case, or if the opposition leads to concepts whose content is meaningless, the correctness of this basic idea seems to us to be subject to serious doubt, at least if our deductions have been made correctly.

We will, therefore, try to derive geographical concepts from

Hettner's and Hartshorne's fundamental idea and from the results of our inquiry recorded in the preceding chapters. Next we will try to ascertain the historical concepts corresponding with particular geographic concepts, starting from the basic idea of the opposition between geography and history. We must leave it to the historian to judge of the significance of these historical concepts.

Although geography and history can be distinguished from each other according to fundamental functions, as Hartshorne [12] says, the significance of the various factual integrations of earthly reality may be different in the two sciences, because these integrations differ in their importance to the geographical and the historical aspects.

Hartshorne says: "In the total reality with which both history and geography are concerned — namely the phenomena of the world in historic times there is one major group of phenomena, the natural phenomena which are causally of fundamental importance to all other phenomena, but which, while differing markedly in different areas of the world, differ but slightly in different periods of historic time — (history in the narrower sense) — ... In consequence, the areal differences that are of greatest importance in geography are either differences in the natural features themselves or in cultural features which are closely related to the natural features. We would have a similar situation in history only if such features as climate and landforms had varied as radically through historic times at the same place, as they vary over the world at the same time" [13].

Although we fully subscribe to Hartshorne's conception that to geography and history the significance of reality is different in connection with the difference in aspect between the two sciences, we should be very careful with regard to the further drift of his argument.

In chapters II and III we have elaborately discussed the fact that the same soil has different possibilities for human subsistence, and that among their various possibilities different soils often have the same possibility for human subsistence in common. Two regions * with similar soils often allow of a differentiation in the way of life, and two regions with different soils often appear to have the same way of life. To a certain extent the same thing holds for the climate. In many cases we can establish a chorological differentiation of economic-geographic integrations, whereas in broad outlines soil and climate are not differentiated. In other regions there is little if any differentiation of the economic-geographic totality, whereas the soils vary.

In the history of the agriculture of a particular area we sometimes meet with a differentiation of arable farming, dairy farming, and horticulture in the course of times, whereas the soil has remained essentially a clay soil. So we can observe an historical change in phenomena that are closely connected with nature without any change in nature itself in the course of the times. We agree with Hartshorne, however, that if the climate of an area should change several times in the course of history, and should more than once vary from moist to dry, and from cold to hot, and if the relief of the soil should differentiate from a plain to a mountain range, the history of the agriculture of that region would change a great deal more.

Hartshorne says that history especially investigates the complicated cultural phenomena, such as social and political phenomena, which are less closely connected with nature and change considerably in course of time, showing a certain development on account of their integration into the passage of time.

---

* In chapters II and III for convenience' sake we have made a further distinction between region and geographic region for the elucidation of the geographic concept region. A region is a chorological unity of one separate thing or of some different things and their phenomena within the earthly complex. A geographic region is a chorological unity of a few interrelated things with their phenomena within the complex, especially of a vertical integration. As the present chapter is concerned with the fundamental aspect of geography, and for this reason chiefly deals with the chorological differentiation of integrations, it is at once clear that by the term region we mean the content of a geographic region. In what is going to follow we have only used the different terms if they were required for further distinctions. In other cases we have as a rule used the word region for the sake of brevity. The stress is then laid on the unity of the chorological extension, in contradistinction to the term "a piece of the earth surface" which is no chorological unity.

Geography investigates the chorological differentiation of the phenomena of nature and those of culture which are closely related to the natural phenomena. We must emphatically point out, however, that the issue is not only concerned with the chorological differentiation of those cultural phenomena that are subject to the influence of nature, but also with those that exert their influence on nature.

Geography deals with the chorological differentiation of nature and culture. As has been explained in great detail, the complex of integrations of nature and culture can be analysed into different integrations, into different unities of totality. The chorological differentiation can, therefore, be further analysed into the various chorological differentiations of the world, each differentiation being based on a definite unity of totality. The chorological differentiation of the world forms, as it were, various mosaics of geographic regions. The degree to which every mosaic can be detailed is very much dependent on our standards of differentiation. These regions are primarily determined and distinguished by the variation of vertical unity of each of them. The chorological differentiation according to the horizontal interconnection and unity, however important it may be, is something secondary.

The mosaic of the regions of every geographic totality is dependent on a definite time, or rather on a definite point of time.

When we consider one single region as a chorological differentiant, we discover that the time during which this region forms a definite geographic unity, may be pretty long. The time during which a geographic region forms a unity might be called a period. That is to say that the structure and the function of the integration, forming a chorological differentiant in a particular part of the world, remain unchanged during that time, and its chorological extension remains the same. As soon as the structure, the function, and the chorological extension undergo an essential change, and a new unity is formed, we speak of another, a following period. As we shall explain in more detail, we should bear in mind, however, that there is some risk in speaking of a period in the sense of a historical concept, when we refer to geographic regions.

Other adjoining geographic regions also form geographic or

105

chorological unities for a longer or shorter period of time. But the periods during which these regions form definite geographic unities are not of equal duration. Suppose the first region had been an arable region for X years, and had gradually changed into a dairy farming region, at present to form a predominantly industrial region after Y years. The contiguous regions had a different course of development. The duration of the geographic unities of the contiguous region A was $X + p$ and $Y + q$ respectively; that of the contiguous region B was $X - 2p$ and $Y - 3q$. So, if we determine a mosaic of geographic regions of the whole world, or of a large part of the world, it will appear that the time during which this mosaic represents regional unities, will be very short. In a particular length of time * a number of regions will form particular unities, but other regions are already undergoing a process of great change, and are passing into new unities, into other chorological differentiants. The chorological differentiation of the whole world into unities of geographic region is often of such a short duration that it is no more than a point of time.

And besides, we should remember that in course of time every geographic region does not change as a unity, and does not develop as a unity. And last but not least, such a region does not maintain the same chorological extension. The fact that as a rule a region does not develop as a unity, has been discussed by Creutzburg as well as by Hartshorne. Creutzburg says: "When we speak of the development, the genesis of a cultural landscape, we should always realize that it is not the landscape as a whole that is subject to change, but only the complex of the changeable elements of a landscape. The development of a cultural landscape is only the development of the complex of its cultural elements" [14]. Among other things Hartshorne says: "Since areas, no matter how small, do not grow as units, but change only as the result of the differential change of different things within them, the unit area of to-day

---

* We prefer to speak of "length of time" and not of "space of time". The issue is here the duration of time and besides, the word space is especially current in geography. A length of time, however, is not always the same thing as a period, a unity of time in a historical sense, as we are going to explain later on.

106

was probably not a unit area in an earlier stage, and will probably not be in a future stage" [15].

But also the chorological extension changes. Let us consider a sea-clay region and an adjoining peat bog region. On the sea-clay sugar beet and wheat used to be grown formerly, and the peat was used for pasture cattle-breeding and dairy farming. There were then two economic-geographic regions. But in course of time the arable farmers on the sea-clay region also came to use the soil for pastural farming. The level of the soil water and the milling of both regions have been coordinated. The old small dairy factory of the peat region was replaced by a large dairy factory, and removed to a point in the vicinity of the border line of the former arable region, which has now entirely been changed into a pastural farming region. The former two different regions now form one economic geographic region [16]. The present geographic region was not a geographic region in the past.

Chorological differentiation resulting in a diversity of geographic regions, in chorological unities, is dependent on a definite time. Geography chiefly and by preference investigates the chorological differentiation of the present time. If the investigation concentrates on the chorological differentiation in the past, we speak of *historical geography*. This is concerned with a mosaic of regions that existed at some time in the past and is valid also for a short time in a cross-section of time. According to the chorological principle the point at issue is not the change and the development of a mosaic of regions in course of time, nor is it the evolutional process of the separate regions. The term historical in historical geography is derived from the term history in its specific sense of the past. It is the geography of a past time [17].

The chorological differentiation of the world forms geographical regions. These geographic regions form unities for a definite time. The unity of every region is in the first place a vertical unity. It is a differentiant, but also a reflection of the totality of the world as a unity. By means of horizontal interconnections based on the relative location of regions and localities, the various regions are connected into larger and smaller wholes. These wholes are relative and in a certain way they form parts of the real whole, viz., the earth surface, or the world as a whole.

The chorological differentiation, however, is not restricted to these vertical unities and their horizontal interconnection. There is also chorological differentiation in the horizontal interconnections, in which attention should first of all be given to the various integrations, to the different unities of geographic totality to which the horizontal interconnections are related. Within a particular integration of the earthly complex there arises also a mosaic of horizontal unities of region. Every region has relative unity, sometimes of a rather loose kind. This unity is determined by a certain equality in relative location (pp. 77 ff). The chorological differentiation of the world then reveals itself in the differentiation of the relative location that forms a mosaic of relative horizontal unities of region. This chorological differentiation of horizontal interconnections of a definite integration or geographic totality, is also bound to a definite period of time, and only partly coalesces with the chorological differentiation of vertical unities of this integration.

The regions of horizontal unity are in their turn interconnected by external horizontal relations which are partly the same as the external horizontal interconnections existing between the vertical unities of region.

If a region of vertical unity is a differentiant and a reflection of the totality of the earthly complex, a region of horizontal unity is a differentiant, and, owing to its internal horizontal interconnection, a reflection of the earth surface (the world) as a whole. The structure (Gliederung) of the world as a whole is, as it were, reflected in the structure of a region with relative internal horizontal unity.

Let us now try to form certain historical concepts from the fundamental contrast between geography and history, and oppose these concepts to those of geography.

The chorological differentiation of a definite integration of phenomena over the earth surface (the world) at a definite time, or at a point of time, has its counter-pole in the differentiation of a definite integration of phenomena in a definite locality in course of time from the remotest past up to the present day. The mosaic of geographic regions of a definite integration at a certain time is opposed to the chain of periods of a definite integration of a locality or of a piece of the earth surface *.

When using the metaphor of a chain, we must immediately admit that this metaphor is defective and incomplete. Yet we will try to explain the historical change and interconnection with the aid of this figure of speech. We imagine this chain to be in a vertical position. Its links are all different, but they belong together and form one whole, one chain. Each link represents the integration in its unity during a certain time, forming a period distinct from the other links of the chain, from the other periods of history. A horizontal cross-section of a link shows us, as it were, the chorological extension of the integration at that period **.

In the comparison of the geographical mosaic with the historical chain we can oppose a chorological unity, a chorological differentiant, or geographic region, to a unity of historical change, a period. Just as a region can only be determined by its difference from other contiguous regions, a period can only be ascertained by its difference from the previous and the next period. A *period* in a historical sense is a unity of time of a definite integration of differentiated phenomena in a certain piece of the world during the whole of its uniform duration. A *region* in a geographical sense is a chorological unity of a definite integration of differentiated phenomena in its entire uniform extension in a particular time.

If in geography we concentrate on the vertical unity of region, in history we consider the uniformity of an integration of interrelated phenomena in a historical period. Geographical horizontal unity of region is comparable with the interconnection of situations and events at different points of time within one period. They are more closely interconnected within this period than with the situations

---

* We prefer to speak of the history of an integration in a definite *piece of the earth surface* and not of that in an area and a region. These geographical concepts have a very special connotation in our study, which in connection with the history of an integration is not applicable here, as we are going to explain in the sequel.
** This last metaphor is a little strained.

and events of the points of time of the previous and the next period. What is the external horizontal interconnection between the various regions over the earth surface at a particular point of time, uniting these regions into a whole, is the interconnection of the successive periods, the course of history, in a particular small piece of the earth surface. It is the whole of history and its unity.

Just as a geographic region as a unity usually passes into the unity of another region only gradually and in a straggling way, the unity of time, a period, generally changes into another period gradually and irregularly. There are sharp limits of time only in particular cases, e.g., periods that start suddenly, and end abruptly owing to the shock of such events as wars.

As we have established, the unity of a region is bound to a definite time. The historical time unit, the period, however, is bound to a definite piece of the earth surface.

If the historical change and development of an integration is determined from the remotest past up to the present day, the chorological extension of the part of the earth surface where the integration is found, will be very small. Just as the chorological differentiation of the whole of the earth surface into regional unities is restricted to a very short length of time, the unity of the chain of periods of the whole of time is restricted to a small piece of the earth surface. For, if the whole of the history of an integration over a larger part of the earth surface is investigated, it will appear that there is not only one, but there are several chains of periods. It is clear that this depends on our standards of the chorological differentiation of the integration at different times, and of the differentiation of the duration of time into periods of this integration in the different pieces of this larger part of the earth surface.

Both geography and history have to do with location and time, but each in a different way.

In geography the goal is the chora. Its unity must be established by investigation. The time is derived from this unity; it is the length of time during which the region of an integration forms a unity, an essential chorological differentiant. This length of time is a unity, a period only in particular circumstances, as we shall explain presently.

In history things are the other way about. The time, the goal, is a unity, viz., a period determined by investigation. The part of the earth surface where the integration is located, has been derived from the period, the duration of time during which the integration is a unity of time. This piece of the world is only a chorological unity under definite circumstances.

A geographic region is a chorological differentiant of the earth surface (or world), and can only be determined by paying attention to its difference from other contiguous regions. It is distinct from these regions, and connected with these and other regions of the earth surface by horizontal interconnections. A geographic region as a chorological differentiant cannot be considered in itself without paying attention to its difference from others, and to its interconnection with the others, especially with contiguous regions. Its unity in its distinction from, and its interconnection with other regions is bound to a definite time. The time during which these regions are distinguishable as unities and are interconnected with each other, is not the same as the time during which each of these regions separately forms a unity in its history, viz., the time from the moment it comes to the fore as a chorological unity out of the previous period until the moment when it passes into the next period as a different unity. The duration of the corresponding periods of the separate regions is different. Generally it is longer than the length of time that the corresponding periods of the separate regions have in common. The latter length of time determines the duration of time during which the regions are to be distinguished from each other as unities, and are united by horizontal interconnections. This time is comparatively short, and is generally not a period itself, at least not a period in the sense of a unity of time, as is the case with a link of the historical chain. Besides, we can only speak with some reserve of a period during the time in which a single region forms a unity that is distinct from the unity of the same region in a previous period of time and in the next. For, as Creutzburg and Hartshorne have ascertained, a region does not change and develop as a unit, and we add that the chorological extension is often different at different times. The chorological extension of one region as a unity at a particular time sometimes embraces two chorological unities of

111

the preceding period. The historical development and growth of a region as an essential chorological differentiant is possible in certain cases, when, e.g., the territory of a state remains the same for a long time. The state's territory is then considered to be a chorological differentiant in its distinction from the territories of other states. Then it is possible to speak of historical periods of one and the same region (the state), in which case the concept period is taken to mean exactly the same thing as in history.

In history things are the other way round. The unity of time, the period, is that which is sought and can be determined only by means of its distinction from, and its interconnection with previous and subsequent periods. The single chain of periods, the continuous course of time, presupposes that the integration in its historical course and change embraces a part of the earth surface of which the nucleus is the same in its chorological extension. The chorological extension of this nucleus in only small, as we have already explained before, and its extent also depends on the length of time and the number of periods within this length of time over which the course of history extends. In a prolonged course of time the integration over a larger part of the earth surface will yield not one, but several chains of periods, of which the periods of the various chains will be different.

The single chain, the continuous process of the integration from the remotest past up till the present day, presupposes a small part of the earth surface. Usually this is not a chorological unity in the sense of a geographical unity of region. The latter is a unity formed by the uniform extension of a particular integration in a definite time, distinct from, and interconnected with other geographical regional unities.

The extension of the piece of earth surface occupied by the integration in its historical development, depends on the continuity of the integration in the successive periods. The latter are the goal. A horizontal cross-section through the chain of periods in a vertical position determines the extension of the piece of the earth surface in which the integration is found. In different periods the chorological extension of this piece of earth surface will be different. The continuous course of history requires a nuclear area formed by the piece of earth surface which, as it were, owes its existence to the overlapping of the pieces occupied by one and the same integration in the separate periods. It is the piece they have in common in which there is one and the same integration in the succession of time in the continuous historical process. This is not a geographic region. A geographic region is the goal of geography, and is determined by the maximal chorological extension of the vertical and horizontal unity in its distinction from and its interconnection with other geographic regions at a definite time. In this case the time depends on the regional unities in their distinction and interconnection. It is the common length of time in which these regions as unities are distinct from each other and horizontally interconnected.

The difference in significance and function of a chora in history from that in geography is emphasized by the fact that the integrations investigated by the two sciences are often widely different. It may be argued that this is connected with the difference in the functions, i.e., that the integrations differ in significance in connection with the difference between these sciences as regards their fundamental aspects. History especially investigates the integrations that change and grow in course of time; they are above all cultural integrations, which display a less close connection with nature, as we have explained before in accordance with Hartshorne's ideas. The cultural integrations that are significant to geography are chiefly formed by those cultural phenomena that are closely interrelated with nature. In connection with this a geographical region also differs in composition and chorological extension from the piece of the earth surface of an integration which has a fundamental historical function. The piece of the world occupied by an integration in its historical course is usually not a chorological unity. In special cases such a part of the earth surface is in certain respects a chorological differentiant, a geographic region such as e.g., the territory of a state, if it remains the same for a long time.

Generally speaking we can say that the mosaic of the regions of the world formed by geography on the ground of the chorological differentiation of a particular integration in a particular length of time, or at some point of time, is different for different times.

The mosaic of the regions of a particular length of time does not change in its entirety into another mosaic as a whole of the following length of time. This length of time is generally not a period. The chain of periods formed by history on the basis of the change and development of an integration in a definite piece of the earth surface, is as a rule different for the various pieces of the earth surface. The chain of the links of an integration of a particular piece of the world is not congruent with the chains of the links of the integrations in contiguous parts of the world. A horizontal cross-section of the different chains forms pieces of the world, but no geographical regional unities; it does not form an essential chorological differentiation of the world for a definite length of time.

Chorological differentiation is the fundamental aspect of geography, and is directed to the formation of unities of region of a particular integration. The length of time has to be adapted to the mosaic of regions. Change, growth in the course of time, is the fundamental aspect of history, which is directed to the formation of unities of time, periods, of a definite integration. The piece of earth surface occupied by the integration is adapted to the chain of periods.

To complete the comparison of geography and history it is necessary to draw attention to another region in geography, and to another unity of time in history.

In Chapter III we have explained why it is impossible to determine chorological unities according to the complete complex of phenomena differentiating over the earth surface. These unities, however, are approximately ascertainable in the so-called nuclear regions. They are the result of the overlapping of the various mosaics of the geographic regions of the different integrations in a definite time. Such nuclear regions, however, are of little or no importance to geography, as the greater part of the world would then be a no man's land, whereas that part of the world comprises regions of separate integrations that are as important as those of the nuclear regions. In the formation of nuclear regions the chorological differentiation of the separate integrations over the earth surface and the mutual horizontal interconnection over the earth surface is interrupted everywhere.

114

No more is it possible to form periods in history that are distinct unities according to all the integrations of the complicated reality. They can be found approximately, however, in nuclear periods, which are the result of the overlapping of the different periods of the various integrations in one and the same locality, which periods generally have a different duration. Such nuclear periods are of little or no importance to history. Then a very large part of the length of time remains undefined, undiscussed, although this part of the length of time encloses important periods of significant integrations. The continuous course and the historical interconnection of the different periods of the various integrations are then continually interrupted, and broken off.

In the preceding chapters we have explained in great detail that a geographic region is only a limited unity of a simple integration, but that this integration is found in reality only within a complex of integrations in which, and with which, it is interwoven. This complex does not constitute a unity of region. We have been able to say the same thing about the unity of time in history, the period. A period, too, is a unity only in certain respects, of a restricted integration existing in reality only within a complex of integrations. In its historical progress this complex does not show any periods which might constitute unities for all the integrations in their interrelation and interconnection. Region and period are abstractions in this sense.

As we have observed, the mosaic of geographic regions of the whole of the earth surface is of short duration, and the historical chain of periods from the remotest past up to the present day is restricted in its unity and continuity to a small piece of the earth surface. If, however, geographical investigation is to have any meaning, the standards of the change in time for the regions will have to be fixed broadly in order to arrive at a mosaic of regions which will be valid for a longer time. Historical investigation will have to unite the various chains of the history of the integrations in different contiguous localities into one chain in order to arrive at the history of an integration of a piece of the earth surface, which piece is significant to us on account of its larger extension.

So, if geographic and historical investigations are to have any meaning, it will be necessary to ignore various less important differentiations in space and time by means of well-considered compromises. The regional unities and those of time, thus obtained, can be identified on the earth surface in a "definite length of time", and in the historical process of reality in a "definite piece of the earth surface", but they have been greatly simplified as to their contents.

Hartshorne says: "We may make the parallel situation of the two fields complete by saying that, while history is concerned with the integration of phenomena in periods of time, it must recognize more or less separate histories for each major area of the world. Likewise geography, integrating phenomena in areas, recognizes separate geographies of each period of time. Geography in the sense of present-day geography, therefore corresponds to the history of one's own country; historical (past) geographies, to the histories of other countries" [18].

In its broad outlines we can subscribe to this pronouncement, but in connection with our previous exposition we must remark that in history a country, a land, is a geographic unity only approximately, and not in a real sense, and that a length of time in geography is not a historical period in its exact sense.

We have continually spoken of the locality and the piece of the earth surface where the integration is found in its historical progress and its change in time. We have purposely avoided speaking of region. This is a geographical concept. It is not only a geographical unity but also a chorological totality.

In history the issue is not really the history of a country, but that of the integration found in that country, and the history of that with which the integration is concerned, viz., with a whole people or a human group.

Geography concentrates on the chorological differentiation which results in a diversity of geographic regions in a definite time. A region as a chorological unity is an integration of particular phenomena of nature and those of culture, which latter are closely connected with the former. History investigates the change and the growth of

116

integrations of cultural phenomena on a particular piece of the earth surface in the course of time. These integrations are often less closely related with nature [19].

So, if we speak of the history of a country, we really mean the history of a people living in that country. Historical integration differs from that of geography. In the former the emphasis lies on the population. History happens to a people living in a country. A geographical integration is formed by the chorological earthly complex. A country, a land, is a part of the earth surface, or a part of the chorological extension of the earthly complex, and in accordance with definite characteristics of an integration of that complex, such a country (or land) forms a chorological unity, a geographic region.

We should, however, be on our guard against considering land and people as each other's counter-poles because of the difference in aspect between geography and history. We cannot say that the geography of a country is the opposite of the history of a people. Certainly not, for geography is concerned with the chorological differentiation of the nature and culture of the whole earth surface at a particular point of time or in a particular length of time. History concerns the differentiation in time of the culture of a people living on a piece of the earth surface from the remotest past up till the present day.

Chorological differentiation results in lands (countries), which are unities, regions, according to definite characteristics.

The differentiation of time results in periods which are unities according to particular characteristics.

A country (land) as a chorological unity is bound to a definite length of time.

As a unity of time, a period is bound to a definite piece of the earth surface.

So the geographical concept "country" as a geographic region is parallel to the historical concept "period". The historical concept "people", i.e., the people in its generations, is parallel to the geographical concept "the earthly chorological complex of things and phenomena in their extension over the earth surface." The length of time in geography has its historical counter-pole in the

117

piece of the earth surface where the historical integration is found. The entire surface extension of a chorologically differentiating integration in a definite length of time is a geographical concept. Its counter-pole is the historical concept of the entire course of time during which an integration differentiating in time has existed on a particular piece of the earth surface.

In the above exposition we have compared the differentiation and the unity of the history of a piece of the world to a chain. We imagine this chain to be in a vertical position. Its links are all different, but they belong together and form one whole, one chain. Each link represents the integration in its unity during a certain time, forming a period distinct from the other links of the chain, from the other periods of history. A horizontal cross-section of a link shows us, as it were, the chorological extension of the integration at that period. The single chain of periods presupposes that the integration in its historical change and course embraces a part of the earth surface of which the nucleus is the same in its chorological extension.

This picture, however, is incomplete. For, if in historical science we emphasize the history of a *people*, we must bear in mind that the country in which this people lives, has not always remained the same. In a remote past a tribe sometimes migrated to another country. The single chain in a perpendicular position in a definite piece of the world was broken and continued in another piece of the world *.

The geographical counter-pole can also be indicated. The mosaic of regions as a unity representing the chorological differentiation of an integration in a definite time is sometimes interrupted as to its horizontal interconnection. A number of adjacent regions, a part of the mosaic, are entirely different from what they were in a previous time, whereas the regions of the other part have altered little or not at all. The latter part of the mosaic fits in better with

* We spoke of a people in its country. As we have sometimes used the term "country" also in a geographical sense as the chorological complex of earthly things, we had better use the term "native country" to indicate its historical meaning. Consequently, a *native country* is the piece of the world in which a people in its generations has lived for a long time, and of which the nucleus in its chorological extension has remained the same during that time.

the former, and properly speaking, is continued in the former part as this was in the mosaic of the previous time.

So, if the integrations investigated by geography and history are different in certain respects, also in connection with the difference between the fundamental aspects of the two sciences, we must not forget, however, that there is also some similarity: economic geography and economic history are concerned with similar integrations. Of course there is no denying that the integrations in which the ground, the soil, plays an important part are more important to geography than to history. But we must again point out that one and the same soil often possesses different possibilities as regards the way of life, so that there may occur great changes in the way of life in course of time. This means that for economic history, and especially for the history of agriculture, the soil is also important. With reference to geography it is necessary to remember that — although the soil often varies considerably in a chorological respect — in its broad outlines the way of life is often very similar in different regions. This is the result of the fact that different kinds of soil possess and utilize a common possibility of the way of life, among their various possibilities. On the other hand various regions with similar soils may have different ways of life. This means that the significance of the soil in geography should not be over-estimated either.

We must, however, state that the more complicated cultural, social and economic phenomena, which differ both chorologically and temporally, and show little or no connection with the nature of the earth surface, are more important to history than to geography. In our opinion a geography which has little or no connection with the nature of the earth surface can hardly be called geography. Geography is concerned with the differentiation of a chorological totality; but an integration that is chorologically differentiated over the surface of the earth and shows no identifiable relations with the nature of this surface, independent of the question whether this nature varies chorologically or not, is geographically irrelevant.

From the above we cannot but draw the conclusion that in addition to the fundamental difference in aspect there is also some important difference between geography and history as regards the integrations (objects) that are investigated. We must immediately add that this latter difference is again partly connected with the difference in aspect between the two sciences. But the difference of the integrations, the difference between the chorological earthly complex and the cultural complex in relation to a people, is not reducible in every respect to the difference in aspect between geography and history.

There is one more difference between geography and history, which, however, is of a quite different nature. Hartshorne refers to it, saying: "Geography, in the sense of present-day geography, therefore corresponds to the history of one's own country; historical (past) geographies, to the histories of other countries. A practical difference results from the fact that, while the study of foreign histories permits the use of the same methods as the history of one's own country (except for differences in language), the study of past geographies does not permit of the direct field observations of present geography. Further, there is a difference in interest: for reasons that need not here concern us, the people of any time and place have a greater intellectual interest in the history of other countries — both present and past — than in the past geography of their own country" [20].

As to the last sentence, it would be better to speak of the geography of the world in the past than of the geography of one's own country in the past. "Present-day and past geography" refer to the chorological differentiation of the whole earth surface at the present time and for some length of time in the past. It is not the geography of one's own country for some length of time, but the geography of the world for some length of time that is compared with the history of some country (or people) from the remotest past up till the present day.

The difference in method and that in interest, referred to by Hartshorne, is important. Especially the difference in interest is significant, viz., the fact that there is certainly an interest in the history of other countries (or peoples), but little interest in the geography of the past. As far as we can see, there is little or no connection at all here with the difference in the fundamental aspects of the two sciences. Perhaps there is another connection here, which concerns the integration (the object) as such and the temporal order, viz., the interest in the past. We shall revert to this later on.

If geography and history lose sight of their fundamental aspects, the two sciences will hardly be distinguishable from each other apart form a difference in integration: If geography studies the integration of *one* region in a particular time, and pays little or no attention at all to the difference from other regions and to the horizontal interconnection with other regions, especially with contiguous regions, this geography approaches history, if the latter investigates an integration on a piece of the earth surface in *one* period, and ignores the difference of this integration from other integrations, especially from those of the preceding and the following periods and their interconnection.

Various authors, e.g. Kroeber, [21] emphasize in history the integration of concrete phenomena.

No doubt, the issue is the integration of the phenomena at a particular time, but the same thing holds for geography. In geography, too, the integration of the phenomena of a particular region is of essential importance; but on the ground of the geographical principle the integration of a particular region will have to be considered in its difference from the integration of other contiguous regions and in its horizontal interconnection with the latter at a particular time, chiefly at the present time. As the counter-pole of this geographical principle history is concerned with the integration of a period in its difference from and in its interconnection with the integrations of the preceding and following periods in a particular piece of the world, notably one's own native country.

How essential it is to bear in mind the difference in aspect between the two sciences will appear when we consider the different forms of positing a problem which are all of them called historical geography in literature.

We compare region and period with each other. A geographical region is the chorological unity of an integration in a particular length of time, especially in the present time. A period is the unity of an integration in time in a particular piece of the earth surface.

Geography considers a region in its difference from and in its horizontal interconnection with other, especially with contiguous regions in a particular length of time. History views a period in its difference from, and in its interconnection with other periods, especially with the preceding and the following periods in a particular piece of the earth surface.

When we wish to go further into the different interpretations of historical geography, it will be necessary to pay attention to the fundamental difference of the aspect of geography and that of history, especially with respect to the concepts region and period.

All that passes for historical geography in literature might be summarized in three different forms:

1. We consider the chorological differentiation of the world, or of a large part of the world, for a length of time belonging to the past. It is also possible to think of one region in its difference from and horizontal interconnection with surrounding regions for that length of time in the past. This is historical *geography*, the aspect of which is not different from that of present-day geography. Here the concept "historical" can only be understood in the sense of past time.

2. When we compose other geographies of other times of the past than the one mentioned under no. 1 and we pay attention to their difference, we are dealing with historical geography in the current sense of the word. It is geography, but a historical element is added. The attention is indeed concentrated on the chorological differentiation of the vertical interrelations and on the horizontal interconnections at different times, but not exclusively so; it is also directed to the process of change in the course of time, and this is the historical element.

3. If, in addition to the study of the process of their change, the different geographies mentioned under number 2 are also considered in their interconnection in the course of time, in their development, they will give rise to a historical view of geography. But, as a mosaic of geographic regions does not

122

as a whole pass into another mosaic, and a region does not change or develop as a *unity* in its difference and horizontal interconnection with other regions in the course of time, our attention will have to be directed to one region in its change and its interconnection in time. The view of a region as a chorological differentiant in its difference from and horizontal interconnection with other regions in some length of time will have to be relegated to the background. The fundamental function of this third form, therefore, is purely historical. The geographical element is only in evidence in the integration as such. Properly speaking, it is a geographic integration but placed in a historical view. It is a historical geography in which the fundamental element of geography is lacking.

Although in these different forms of historical geography the geographic element is not in evidence in the same way, and to different degrees, we will call these three forms historical geography, because this term is used for these different concepts and has become current.

When in this connection we think of Hartshorne's words, quoted in an earlier context, "the people of any time and place have a greater intellectual interest in the history of other countries — both present and past — than in the past geography of their own country" [22], we can say: The scientific interest in the various forms of historical geography shows very great differences. The form mentioned under 1. arouses our interest but little; that under 2. interests us moderately, but there is a greater interest in the third form of historical geography. This is entirely in agreement with Hartshorne's observation. For in this last form of historical geography the aspect is historical. Whether this part of the world is another country (people), or our own, is not very important to our historical interest. In the historical geographies under 1. and 2. the aspect is geographical, although more pronounced in 1. than in 2. There is little scientific interest in the geography of the past, either of one's own or of another country.

However fundamental the difference in aspect of geography and history may be, the integration (the object), the temporal order, and the temporal character are also significant. The interest in matters of geography and history is, in our opinion, often based on a combination of aspects, integrations (objects) and temporal order, viz., past time. Consider a geologist. He is interested in the historical aspect, in the process of change and development in time, and in the past, but he is also interested in geographical integration as such, in the complex of the earth surface. He directs the historical aspect to the earth surface of the past. But he has little interest in the geographical aspect: the chorological differentiation and the chorological horizontal interconnection of the earth surface in a particular length of time of the past. What can be said about a geologist and geology, also holds for palaeontology and palaeoclimatology, although perhaps to a less degree. We have made an inquiry into the chorological differentiation of land forms, climate and vegetation at the end of the tertiary period. Little has been written about it. On the other hand a great deal has been written about these phenomena of the earth surface in general or of a definite part of the earth surface in that time, but there is considerably less interest in the difference of the various areas of the earth surface in this geological period.

In the third form of historical geography we have just now seen one and the same combination attracting the attention, viz., the historical aspect, the past, and geographic integration as such. When we think of the counter-pole of this form of historical geography, we also discover a field of science in which there is a great interest, which, however, is formally based on a remarkable combination. We are referring to the foreign policy of a state (a nation) in one particular length of time of the past. The integration as such is historical, and, besides, it is found in a particular time in the past, but the emphasis is not laid on the historical aspect. The issue is not so much the process of the change and development of that policy in the course of time, but rather that policy for a definite length of time. The foreign policy of a state essentially implies a geographical function: for here such problems are discussed as the policy of a state in its chorological difference from and horizontal interconnection with other, especially with contiguous states. A historian will perhaps be unaware of the geographical aspect of his inquiry. In his case the interest in the past and in political relations between nations in the same length of time is predominant, and the prevailing tendency is to assign this field to the science of history.

Consequently the interest is not exlusively kept within the line of demarcation of the aspects of geography and history. In reality there are combinations of aspects and integrations (objects) in which the aspect of history is connected with the integration of geography, and vice versa, while the interest in the past also plays its part. However, this is of course no solution of the problem, why there is so little interest in the geographic aspect of the geographic integration in a length of time of the past (the chorological differentiation and the horizontal interconnection of the things of nature and those of culture which are connected with nature, in the past). It remains a remarkable fact that the interest in history is much more comprehensive than that in geography. A historian is interested in the historical aspect, in the past and in the historical integration, viz., the people, and not only in his own people but also in other nations. A geographer is interested in the geographical aspect in connection with the geographical integration, i.e., the chorological differentiation of the complex of the earth surface, but his interest is very definitely focused on the time in which he lives. He takes an interest in the earth surface, and in the world on and in which he lives. The world of the past viewed in its *geographical aspect* appeals to him much less.

If we wish to distinguish geography and history purely as sciences, it seems necessary to emphasize the aspects of the two sciences [23]. In connection with this we have continually argued in the above that in geography a region cannot be isolated. A region is a chorological differentiant of the earth surface or world. We are, therefore, concerned with this region in its difference from and its interconnection with contiguous regions. When we look upon a region as a chorological differentiant of the earth surface we refer in the first place to a larger region that is still significant with respect to the whole of the earth surface. A smaller region must be viewed in its difference from and its horizontal interconnection with contiguous smaller regions within a larger one. The principle is the same, but there is a difference in proportions. But we are of the opinion that geography is the science of the chorological differentiation of the earth surface, and that the investigation should be directed as much as possible to regions of such proportions that the connection with the terrestrial world as a whole does not get lost. We also think that the concept "period" in history presupposes the connection with the whole of history.

In comparing geography with history it is also necessary to bear in mind the proportions of the concepts "region" and "period". Of this Hartshorne gives a striking example. It is as follows: "If we imagine a series of air photographs taken of a single area in England, and from the same point in the air, on a mid-summer day every year during the past twenty centuries, and viewed as a motion picture film by geographers and historians, the historians would quite possibly consider it a historical picture, but certainly geographers would call it geographic. Each would see different things in the picture. To the geographer, this would be a presentation of areal variation as it changed through time; if every individual photograph is geographic, surely the series as a whole is geographic" [24].

If we have understood Hartshorne correctly, the issue is here the chorological differentiation within one area, and the variations of the chorological differentiation of this area at different points of time. Then we would only remark that, although the whole series, all the pictures, one by one, are geographic, the aspect "as it has changed through time" is historical. The latter aspect is not so much concentrated on the chorological differentiation of that area of each picture apart, but rather on a part of this area or on that area as a whole of those two thousand pictures in its change during those twenty centuries.

But we are concerned with the exact proportions of the chorological differentiation and the differentiation in time, and they have been stated clearly: the finer chorological differentiation within an area is compared with the finer differentiation in time, viz., the small changes that have taken place every year during these

126

twenty centuries. This area in England is only a small part of the earth surface as a whole, just as the twenty centuries form only a small length of time in the whole of the history of this area, in which palaeontology together with pre-history far exceed historic time in the narrower sense of the word. If, however, we emphasize the anthropocentric character of both geography and history, the extension of the earth surface as a human habitat is comparable with the duration of the time of human history. The immense duration of the time of palaeontology falls outside of it. In this case the length of time of twenty centuries as compared with the whole of human history is longer than the surface extension of the area in England is in comparison with the whole of the earth surface.

As to the correct relation between chorological extension and historical duration of time generally, we think we may say what we said before, viz., that the whole of the surface extension occupied by a chorologically differentiating integration at a certain time is a geographic concept, as compared with the historical concept of the whole temporal duration of an integration differentiating in time on a particular piece of the earth surface.

When we make a sharp distinction between the different aspects of geography and history in their different functions, we do not mean to say that the investigations of geography do not take account of the historical aspect of a region. On the contrary; this is even indispensable in most cases, but it is not an aim in itself. It is a means to a better understanding of a region at the present time.

We can and must sharply distinguish between the aspects of geography and history, but we should immediately add that, to a greater or less degree, one and the same integration possesses a geographic and an historical function at the same time. They can be distinguished within that integration, but they cannot be separated from each other in reality.

A region as a unity in its difference from and its horizontal interconnection with other regions in a cross-section of time is in reality an abstraction. However small we may make the length of time, the chorological integration in its structure, function, and chorological extension is not at rest. This integration is at the same time subject to change and growth in time.

The study of the chorological differentiation and interconnection of the world, therefore, always requires us to take account of the process of change and development to which this chorological differentiation of the world is also subject. That is to say that the process of change and development in the past is significant to the chorological differentiation at the present time. In each case the question as to how far it will be necessary to go back in history, requires different answers, which also depend on the nature of the phenomena. Some of these, such as the atmosphere, and the hydrosphere, are very mobile. With the appearance and the disappearance of particular causes, their effects come and go shortly after them. For in the state of affairs at this moment only the effects and their causes of the time immediately preceding it make themselves felt. The functional integration at this moment is based on the present forces, and the integration is fairly complete. The geographic integrations of morphological, organic, social, economic, cultural and political phenomena, however, are of a different character. In them the state of affairs at the present time cannot be exclusively explained from the effects of the present. Even though the causes of earlier influences have long ceased to exist, their effect has continued. A new influence does not affect a neutral state of affairs, but a state determined by causes of the past. The new influences are added to the old ones. Many old effects, however, will be incorporated into the new integration only with difficulty, because they no longer fit in with them, and as relics they do not participate in the new integration [25].

It is necessary to have knowledge of the process of change and development, but it is not a purpose in geography [26]. Various authors, such as Bobek and Schmithüsen [27], Jones [28], and Clark [29], lay a very strong emphasis on this process of development in geography. This, however, puts the difference between the fundamental aspects of geography and history in the background.

With respect to history the same remark can be made. However small the locality of an integration is in its process of change and development, this integration is at the same time connected with

128

the integrations of other localities by means of horizontal chorological interconnections. The chain of periods of an integration in
one locality is not independent of the chains of periods of other
integrations in other localities, but at every point of time these
chains are connected by the horizontal chorological interconnection.
This horizontal interconnection is above all determined by the
chorological differentiation, by the difference between these integrations of different localities in the same length of time.

Geographical investigation has to avail itself of the historical
function, and history must include the geographic function in its
investigation.

The chorological differentiation of the world — the difference
between its regions — is to a high degree decisive of the horizontal
interconnection of the regions, and this interconnection constitutes
the unity of the world (Chapter V).

The differentiation of time into periods is also characterized by
the interconnection of these periods, by a process of growth. In
this connection we would ask: Is it possible that this historical
interconnection, this process of growth, is strongly determined by
the differentiation of time, by the difference between the periods?

In our opinion chorological differentiation is the primary principle of geography, on which the chorological interconnection is
chiefly based. We are not competent to state that also in history the
fundamental function is the change in time, the difference between
the various periods, on which especially the interconnection of the
periods, the process of growth is based. We must leave such a judge-
ment to the historian.

Although chorological differentiation is the primary geographic
element, and the horizontal interconnection is very much dependent
on it, the latter also has a considerable influence on the former.
The character of the products of an economic-geographic region
in its difference from other economic-geographic regions is also
determined by the demand for particular products on the part of
these regions. The horizontal interconnections of these regions with
the former region, therefore, partly determine the peculiarity of
that region, they constitute that region as a chorological differentiant in a definite length of time.

129

The horizontal interconnections are also very important for the unity of the chorological differentiation. These interconnections create a certain similarity of the chorological differentiants, which, however, again display great differences in other respects and are chorological differentiants. We are thinking of the horizontal unity of a state. Owing to the horizontal interconnections between the different regions of a state these regions, these parts of a state, assume a certain amount of similarity. The unity and uniformity of administration, laws, regulations and culture, and also the interconnections of the parts, bring about a large measure of similarity. History, as it were, shows the counter-pole of this geographic concept in historical tradition. However different the periods may be, the historical interconnection unites various periods of the historical chain so that, in addition to great differences, these periods also display a certain amount of similarity in customs, usage, and the conditions of spiritual culture. In a definite course of time tradition, handed down from generation to generation, gives rise to some unity and similarity between the material and the immaterial things of an integration.

In summary we can say that although chorological diversity is the primary principle in geography, and is very important for horizontal interconnection, this horizontal chorological interconnection, is also very important for the character of the chorological differentiation. The horizontal interconnection combines the *different* chorological differentiants into a unity. Besides, the chorological differentiants of contiguous regions display a certain similarity in some respects owing to the horizontal interconnection, and are combined into a unity as similar parts of a whole. If chorological differentiation is the primary principle, the horizontal chorological interconnection together with this differentiation also constitute mutually functional principles.

The same thing may hold for the differentiation into periods and the historical interconnection of these periods.

With respects to geography we should add the following: the geographical aspect leaves time unchanged and constant, i.e., a particular chorological differentiation, and a particular horizontal interconnection, remain essentially the same and do not change during a definite length of time; but during that length of time there is certainly question of temporal succession. For in defining the significance of the chorological differentiation and of the horizontal interconnection, we have called attention to the primary effect of the chorological differentiation of the vertical interrelations, and afterwards to the effect of the horizontal interconnections. At a certain moment both these factors operate simultaneously, but the nature of their operation displays a succession in time. The length of time during which this rhythmical succession of operations remains unchanged and does not essentially alter, is the duration of time in which a region forms a *unity* in difference from, and in horizontal interconnection with other regions.

Finally we will briefly consider what, in our opinion, is the meaning of the aspect and the function of chorological differentiation.

Reflecting on the meaning of geography, our thoughts turn especially to Ritter, who had reflected on it more than any other geographer. In recent years there have appeared important treatises on Ritter's geography, also after the studies by Hözel [30] and Plewe [31]. We are referring to a study by Schmitthenner [32] and to an article by Van Paassen [33].

Ritter's geography is very complicated. Viewed from our standpoint, the way we have distinguished between the geographical and the historical aspect, Ritter's ideas are a combination of these two aspects with views derived from his outlook on life. According to many people Ritter's metaphysical and religious views have been detrimental to his scientific work. Schmitthenner, however, convincingly shows that this is not the case, and that, on the contrary, Ritter's view of the world overarches, as it were, his scientific geographical work and has made his study fruitful [34].

Ritter's geography is anthropocentric. Van Paassen points out that Ritter's anthropomorphism was not a principle derived from his view of life and the world, but a scientific principle [35]. In geography Ritter is concerned with the earth as the habitation of man. This is an important point, as we have elaborately explained in Chapter III. But we must add that Ritter not only saw the earth as a dwellingplace (Wohnhaus), but also as an educational home of

131

the human race (Erziehungshaus des Menschengeschlechtes), and this was a principle derived from his view of life and the world.

Van Paassen contends that Ritter had already formulated Hettner's chorological principle [36]. True, Ritter emphatically brought to the fore the chorological differentiation of the vertically interrelated earthly complex, the relative location and the horizontal interconnection of localities and regions. He laid emphasis on the morphological phenomena. In his view of a part of the world (continent) — which he conceived of as a terrestrial individual (Erdindividuum) — the morphological phenomena, in their differentiation and horizontal interconnection, were the determining factors. Especially the horizontal interconnection within a continent (Erdteil), the grouping of earth spaces (tellurische Anordnung), was stressed [37].

But as we have already observed, the historical and the geographical aspect are closely interwoven in Ritter's thought. His conceptions of the integration of the phenomena of nature and culture can be interpreted in different ways. He speaks of a chorological totality, and also of the relation of man to nature as an original primary datum [38]. But in our opinion there is no doubt possible that again and again Ritter included the phenomena of vertical interrelation and horizontal interconnection in a historical view: The earth as the habitation of the human race, a people in its country, the significance of relative location, are ultimately viewed in the process of their development and growth, and in particular relative location in its change in course of time. The principle of finality and Ritter's idea of purpose (Zweckgedanke) are historically rather than geographically oriented [39].

If, however, we wish to distinguish the geographical aspect from the historical aspect, and see the geographic function in the chorological differentiation and the horizontal interconnection of the earthly complex in a definite length of time, we must say that this function is not very marked in Ritter.

The chorological differentiation of the vertical and the horizontal integrations results in different geographic regions at a particular time. On the one hand they can be distinguished from each other according to differences in vertically interrelated phenomena, and on the other hand according to differences in internal horizontal interconnection, in relative location. These regions, these relative vertical unities and horizontal unities (unities of relative location) are interconnected by horizontal relations, so that we can speak of the unity and the structure (Gliederung) of the world in a particular space of time.

Placing the anthropocentric character of geography in the foreground, we think it important to know whether or not the nature of the earth surface displayed a chorological diversity at the time when man made his entry into the world as the most important inhabitant of the earth. The scarce data of the chorological differentiation of the earth surface supplied by geology, palaeontology, and palaeo-climatology enable us to say that during the change from the tertiary to the quaternary period there was indeed a chorological differentiation of the landforms, the climate, vegetation and fauna.

We can certainly not say that if particular phenomena of nature have a strong influence on culture, the chorological differentiation of these natural phenomena simply determines the chorological differentiation of the cultural phenomena too (Chapter II). But we can indeed say that the chorological differentiation of nature strongly promotes the chorological differentiation of particular cultural and economic phenomena.

So, if in that time when man was created, there was some chorological differentiation of the earth surface which was maintained in the next period of time, although there occurred great changes in it, we must consider it as something normal that the development of different cultural phenomena displayed some chorological differentiation. This posits the condition that it was possible for the human race in its passive and active adaptation to the diversity of the nature of the earth surface to show chorological differentiations. We consider the diversity of the chorological complex of nature and culture to be normal and one of the treasures inherent in the creation.

The genetic and the historical origin of the diversity of culture under the influence of the diversity and the possibilities of nature is not a geographic problem.

133

Geography studies the chorological differentiation of this earthly complex within a definite length of time. The issue is not only the influence of nature on culture at a particular time, chiefly at the present time, but also the influence of culture on nature. In many cases the latter is more important than the former. The influence of nature on certain economic and political phenomena is often difficult to ascertain; but the influence of economic life and of the economic and political policy of the state on material culture, and via this material culture on nature, viz., on the soil, on vegetation and to a less degree on climate (hothouse climate), is very great.

The same thing holds for many spiritual phenomena. It seems difficult for us to establish a relation between the chorological differentiation of the natural condition of Europe and the chorological differentiation of the Christian confessions of this part of the world. In fact, according to our conviction true religion remains unaffected by the diversity and the possibilities of nature. The message of the Gospel is the same to all human beings, to people living in fertile areas and to those in barren areas, to people in hot and in cold, dry and wet regions, to people living in low lands and to those in the mountains. This is not saying that the Gospel is interpreted in the same way everywhere. On the contrary, the various confessions prove the opposite. Historical and political relations have been more significant than the physical condition of Europe. But the chorological diversity of the Christian religion even now has a great influence on the chorological differentiation of material culture, and via the latter also on the differentiation of the natural environment in Europe.

In other religions, and also in the diversity of Christian popular belief, however, the influence of the diversity of nature can certainly be discerned. But in our opinion there is in this case a far greater influence ascertainable in the opposite direction, viz., the great influence of religious on economic phenomena, on material culture, and on natural environment [40]. So if in geography the issue is concerned with cultural phenomena that are interrelated with nature, the interest is not only focused on the significance of nature to culture, but also on the influence of culture on nature.

Geography is concerned with the continuum of the earth surface

134

in its manifold diversity. The purpose of geography is to determine the essential chorological differentiants: countries and regions [41]. As its investigation will never embrace the chorological differentiation of the whole of the earth surface, but only a small part of it except in global studies, geographical investigations focus on an area, on a region. Then the problem is: what is this region like, and what are its relations with other, especially with surrounding regions at the time in which we live? In both cases the principle of chorological differentiation is of fundamental importance.

What a region is like is determined by its characteristics. They can only be established by comparison with contiguous regions from which it is distinguished. Precisely on account of the characteristics that distinguish it from other regions, it is this particular region. A region must be defined and considered as a chorological differentiant. Owing to its difference from other regions this particular region as a chorological differentiant has relations, horizontal interconnections, with other regions, in which its relative location with respect to the others, to contiguous regions, is an important factor.

The movement, the horizontal interconnection, is chiefly caused by the difference between the things and their phenomena of the various places on the earth: The atmospheric circulation is due to differences in atmospheric pressure, and the goods trade is especially based on the difference between these goods. Only then can the horizontal interconnection bring about a certain amount of similarity.

A part of the earth surface as a chorological differentiant has in the first place been formed by the maximal uniform extension of particular integrated phenomena. This is the vertical unity of a region formed by a differentiation of one single integration of the earthly complex, leaving the finer differentiation of the integration in that region out of account. Via the external horizontal interconnections this region enters into relation with other regions. In a restricted sense a region is part of a whole of regions.

If we consider a part of the earth surface in its unity of internal horizontal interconnections, the uniformity of the relative locations of the places and the parts of a region come to the fore. This hori-

135

zontal unity is formed by the maximal extension of the unity of relative location. This unity of relative location, too, is based on particular integrated phenomena of the earthly complex. This internal horizontal unity is characterized both by a certain degree of similarity and a certain degree of dissimilarity in the vertical composition of the parts of a region. In a limited sense we can speak of the parts of a whole.

Both vertical and horizontal unity are concerned with the maximal uniform extension of the chorological differentiant; for the issue is the formation of a region in its distinction from contiguous regions. A portion of this chorological differentiant, a part of this region, either in its vertical composition, or in its relative location, is equal to the other parts of that region. So this portion is not distinct from the other parts of that region. In other words, these parts are not the result of chorological differentiation, and are no regions themselves, no chorological differentiants.

On the ground of the different integrations there are different regions to be determined in the manifold diversity of the earthly complex both of vertical and of horizontal unity. These regions depend for their size on the standards applied to the chorological differentiation. In connection with the anthropocentric character of geography it is especially the significance of the region (territory) of the state that comes to the fore.

The characteristic feature of geographic phenomena is the chorological totality and the chorological whole. The different phenomena are vertically interrelated at every point of the earth, and the phenomena of different earthpoints are horizontally interconnected with one another. In both we see, as it were, a reflection of the unity of the world. It is especially on account of the latter characteristic that the geographic aspect, the chorological differentiation, becomes meaningful.

Via the external horizontal interconnections a region as a vertical unity, as a chorological differentiant, is directed to other regions, especially to contiguous regions, and forms a comparative whole with them. This direction to each other in a definite time we would like to call *chorological finality*. Placing the anthropocentric character of geography in the forefront, we are of opinion that this chorological finality is the meaning and the norm of geography. But this finality is above all determined by the difference between the regions, by their chorological differentiation.

A region as a chorological differentiant, as a chorological particularity, is related with other regions, with other chorological particularities. This region participates in the diversity of a larger or smaller part of the world. This region distributes things belonging to it, and in return it receives what is peculiar to other regions, works this up again, is enriched by it, and re-distributes it to other regions. Owing to the principle of chorological finality a region fills and replenishes the earth.

We look upon the chorological diversity of the world as one of the treasures of the creation, but this treasure is done justice to only, if this diversity forms a unity. The distinction, the difference, between regions may bring about and strengthen this unity, but the differentiation, the difference, may also destroy the unity. A country that isolates itself and becomes selfcontained, does not share in the blessings of the diversity of other countries. The limit to the appreciation of what is peculiar to our own country is exceeded. What is peculiar to our own region is overestimated, and the value of what is peculiar to other regions is rejected. The difference between our own region and other regions is degraded into a contrast. The reverse is also possible: then the unity is so much overrated that the diversity is levelled and degraded into some monotonous equality.

Chorological teleology is not only manifested in human geographic phenomena, but also in physico-geographic phenomena. The teleology of the latter is more restricted, however, and only bears the character of suitability (Zweckmässigkeit). We are referring to atmospheric circulation, ocean currents, and rivers. Owing to the winds there is an exchange of heat and cold, moisture and drought, between the various regions, uniting the different climatic regions into a system. Winds, ocean currents and rivers carry soil particles from one region to another, so that the soils of different regions are more or less interconnected.

In human geographic phenomena chorological teleology has been fully developed. Here we speak of the striving after an aim

(Zielstrebigkeit). The exchange of material and immaterial goods, emigration and immigration, which are based on modern and on primitive traffic, combine regions more or less into larger and smaller wholes [42].

Chorological teleology, giving unity to chorological differentiation, has a different significance in each of the various regions. Primitive regions entertain only restricted relations with surrounding regions. Modern regions, on the other hand, embrace the whole world in their relations, but the chorological finality in both of them is essentially the same. There is only a quantitative difference in connection with the possibilities of material and spiritual technique.

Chorological finality is not a one-sided but a mutual principle. One region is directed to other regions, and the latter are directed to the former. Our conviction is, that this state of affairs implies the norm of geography, of chorological differentiation. A region may or may not conform to this norm. It answers its purpose if it develops its own peculiarity, but not exclusively for its own benefit. It should also let other regions share in it. As this requirement is not one-sided, but mutual, i.e., holds for every region, every region receives something of what is peculiar to other regions in return. Thus every region shares in the rich diversity of the world and fills and replenishes the earth. Then the unity of the world is reflected in its diversity. This requirement comes to the fore in every length of time, and is based on the diversity within the unity, and on the unity in the diversity of the human race and the nature of the earth surface.

There is no length of time in which a region fully answers this requirement. There are forces in one's own region and in other, contiguous regions that disturb the unfolding of what is peculiar in one's own region in relation to the other regions.

However, the chorological differentiation of the earth does not exist in and by itself, but is sustained by divine energies. And although the dark shadow of the curse resting on the creation is clearly discernible in the antithesis into which the chorological differentiation of many regions has degenerated, the wealth implied in this earthly diversity has not been destroyed by the curse. On the contrary, owing to divine grace the harmony of the unity in the

138

diversity in various regions has become manifest at every point of time [43].

To our mind geography should use the harmony of what is particular, the unity in the diversity, as the standard of its evaluation of the chorological differentiation of the world in the time in which we live [44].

CHAPTER VII

THE GENERAL AND THE SPECIAL WITHIN
THE CHOROLOGICAL DIFFERENTIATION

The chorological differentiation of the earthly complex is infinite, but it is also a fact that various differentiations of different areas display some similarity. Many differentiations belong to one and the same type, and with some reservation it is possible to speak of differentiations as members of a class, a class which is again sub-divided into sub-classes, and sub-classes which in their turn are included into a class via some classification.

General or systematic geography busies itself with these problems. With the aid of generic concepts * it tries to systematize the infinite differentiation. Special or regional geography, investigating and describing the constellation of a chorological integration of an area, or of a geographic region, in its speciality, does so with the aid of the generic concepts procured by general geographic investigation. Very often the characteristic of regional geography consists in the special combination of generic concepts, in particular of fundamental (basic) concepts by means of which special concepts are formed.

But in what is general and in what is special in a chorological differentiation there is another problem implied. The chorological differentiation of the earthly complex, and of its component integrations results in geographic regions that are distinct from each other. The difference of the regions is expressed in the different characteristics of these regions. The characteristics expressed in generic and special concepts are connected with each other. Consequently, although these characteristics are not apart from each other, but are mutually connected, they are certainly not equally significant. One characteristic is more important than another.

When we investigate the climate of an area and suppose that

* Here and in what follows "generic" is used in its logical, and not in its biological sense.

it belongs to the type, or possibly to the class of the savannah climate, we chiefly think of three characteristics, viz., tropical heat, humidity and a further determination of this humidity, consisting in an interruption of a wet period by a short dry period. Each of these characteristics has a different significance. The greater or less great significance of each characteristic, however, is also connected with the question in what respect and for what other things and phenomena the significance of this climate is being investigated.

Three juxtapositional regions: an arable region, a pastoral farming region, and an industrial region are distinct from each other on account of different characteristics, but the characteristics distinguishing these regions from each other are not of the same value. The difference between the arable and the pastoral farming region is smaller than the difference between these two and the industrial region. The two former regions have something in common, viz., the agrarian characteristics distinguishing them from the industrial characteristic of the third region.

A part of a state is distinct from the other parts of this state on account of various characteristics; but these parts also have some characteristics in common. They are the characteristics that differentiate the state from other adjoining states.

This grading of the significance of the different characteristics of the regions is very important both for general and for special geography. The ascertainment and determination of the importance of the characteristics must be based on comparison, and this investigation belongs to the domain of general geography. The problem of the grading of the importance of the distinctive characteristics of the regions is closely connected with the division and the classification of the geographical general concepts.

During the first few decades of this century the difference between general and special geography was considered to be of fundamental importance.

This was chiefly connected with the idea of a supposed essential difference between the sciences that deal with what is general and those that are concerned with what is special in the phenomena. The German philosophers Windelband and Rickert have formulated

141

this idea [1]. Rickert has elaborated this idea systematically [2]. Both of them distinguish the sciences on the ground of a difference in their formation of concepts. Windelband spoke of nomothetic and idiographic concepts. The former, the generic concepts, are formed by the natural sciences; the latter, the special concepts, are the domain of the cultural sciences. This is why Rickert spoke of natural-scientific and cultural-scientific concepts. In the former our reflection is concentrated on what is general, similar, on what is according to a law, on that which possesses a certain inevitability, and on that which is neutral with respect to value (wertfrei). The latter are concerned with what is special, with that which is distinctive and is important for us owing to its significance in connection with ideal values (wertbeziehend).

It should be observed, however, — what Rickert actually does in his second work — that the cultural sciences also avail themselves of general concepts sometimes. In the descriptive natural sciences special concepts are also applied.

On the ground of Rickert and Windelband's distinction general geography is rather a nomothetic science, and special (or regional) geography is an idiographic science; meanwhile various fields show a transition between the two methods of forming concepts. Graf [3] has made an elaborate and systematic analysis of the geographical sciences on the ground of the methods of forming concepts.

According to Eucken [4] during the last few decades the development of the theory of science has not gone in the direction in which the distinction between the nomothetic and the idiographic formation of concepts has been of decisive importance.

As early as in the first few decades of this century Hettner [5] was of the opinion that this distinction in the formation of concepts is not decisive with respect to the *aspect* and the problems of geography. Hartshorne [6] discusses the two kinds of concepts in geography in great detail, and maintains the fundamental aspect of geography which forms the basis both of general and of special geography. Some years ago we also wrote about these problems and tried to elaborate the basic ideas of Hettner and Hartshorne [7].

There was, however, also another reason why some twenty

142

years ago a fundamental difference was ascribed to general and special geography. General geography chiefly occupied itself with separate earthly things and phenomena and examined them as such in their distribution. The idea of the totality of the geographic phenomena of a region was thereby pushed entirely into the background. Special geography, on the other hand, emphasized this totality of the phenomena in a region [8].

In recent years the character of general and that of special geography has again been investigated by Hartshorne [9], Schmitthenner [10], Bobek [11] and by us [12]. For the present we shall restrict ourselves to the first two authors.

If we have understood Hartshorne correctly, his argument boils down to the following [13].

There are two methods of analysing geographic phenomena:

1. The complex of earthly phenomena is analysed into less complicated integrations, each with a closer interrelation of the phenomena in one locality, and with a stronger interconnection between the different localities.

2. The earth surface, or rather a part of it, is divided into small regions within which the chorological variation is of a restricted nature. These regions have greater unity and uniformity as to a particular integration, and a greater interconnection of the phenomena between the localities of every region. In such regions the complex of phenomena can be investigated better, because there is greater unity.

General geography starts from the former method: "topical division into segments"; regional geography starts from the latter: "regional division into sections". The comparative method of investigating the earth surface about one single phenomenon out of the complex, and the inquiry into the most complicated integration in one small region are the extremes of the two methods. They do not form a contrast, however, but are connected with each other via many transitional cases. The greater the degree to which the analysis of the complex of phenomena is carried, the smaller the degree of regional division needs to be, and with the increase of the complication of an integration (segment) a more detailed regional division is required [14]. Neither for a "topical division"

143

nor for a "regional division" is there any standard system possible. For a topical division the standard is that as much as possible those phenomena are joined together in one segment which display the highest degree of similarity in chorological differentiation. For this suggests the existence of a close integration of the phenomena, of the dependence on a common determining factor [15]. In the application of the two methods, however, we should take account of the fact that every "topical segment" forms an unbreakable part of the complex of phenomena, and that every region is connected with other regions and forms a part of the continuum of the earth surface [16]. This is Hartshorne's view.

Although on the ground of different considerations, Schmitthenner partly arrives at the same conclusion as Hartshorne. He states: "General geography makes a comparative study of the phenomena over the earth surface and composes the system of concepts of geography. Whereas regional geography (Länderkunde) has to investigate regions and landscapes by applying the geographical concepts, general geography gains an insight into the different spatial phenomena and arrives at the regional unities of the individual factors. The course of the investigation is different in each of the two parts of geography. Regional geography proceeds from what is spatial to things (vom räumlichen zum sachlichen), general geography proceeds from things to the spatial principle (vom sachlichen zum räumlichen Prinzip). There we start from spatial complexes, here from special things (vom sachlichen Speziellen aus)" [17]. "Regional geography (Länderkunde) and general geography join hands when the former distinguishes the spatial in the general, and the latter recognizes the general in the spatial" [18].

Both methods are regional, Hartshorne rightly observes. But we would add that both methods also require a previous analysis of the complex of phenomena (topical division). In this respect we cannot detect any difference between general and special geography. How is one to ascertain smaller regions of greater uniformity in special or regional geography, if one does not first analyse the complex of phenomena, and directs one's attention to some integrations, or necessarily to one integration? Smaller regions of the greatest

144

uniformity can only be ascertained by concentrating on the chorological differentiation of one single integration.

We can understand Hartshorne's argument, nevertheless. It is clear that he sharply distinguishes between an area and the complex of things and their phenomena found in this area. Our view is different: the complex of things in its dimensions of a particular absolute and relative location is identical with the area of this particular absolute and relative location (Chapter II). The chorological differentiation of this area, the division of this area into smaller more uniform regions, is the chorological differentiation of this complex of things in complexes of smaller dimensions with greater uniformity of particular integrations of the complex.

As the complex of things does not chorologically differentiate in a uniform way, we direct our attention to a few things of the complex that are closely integrated and which differentiate in an approximately uniform way which depends on our standards. These interrelated things, however, are parts of the whole complex with which they are interwoven. If in special geography we speak of a number of geographic regions in a particular part of the world, we have in reality chorologically differentiated the whole complex of things there on the ground of some particular characteristics of a few interrelated things of this complex, which things are differentiated in the same way. These geographic regions have been determined by the two dimensions of the surface of the chorological differentiations of those particular things of the complex. The chorological extension of a geographical region is determined by the absolute uninterrupted extension of the ground on and in which the chorological differentiations of these things are spread in greater or less density, independent of the question as to whether or not this ground already forms a chorological differentiation. As the chorological differentiations of a thing in their extension often form a continuum, the regions of these differentiations will differ in extent and form in accordance with the nature of the characteristics of this thing that are used as standards for its chorological differentiation. The atmosphere of a part of the earth surface, in the case of a distinction between essential quantitative values of temperature, will show climatic regions of an extent and form that differ

145

from the climatic regions determined in that part of the earth surface according to the chorological differentiation of the atmosphere
on the basis of essential quantities of precipitation. If in the first
place this is important for the chorological differentiation of the
separate things of the complex, it is also important for the chorological differentiation of a number of interrelated things of the
complex that are investigated by special geography (Chapters II
and III).

General and special geography both have to do with the reality
of the earthly complex, which differentiates chorologically. To
ascertain this chorological differentiation we must analyse the
complex, although general geography carries the analysis further.
Only after this analysis are we able to investigate the chorological
differentiation. This chorological differentiation results in geographic regions. General geography is concerned with the chorological differentiation of the whole of the earth surface, or with
a large part of it. So, if we speak here of large geographic regions,
of chorological differentiants, we have in reality differentiated the
complex of things chorologically on the ground of some characteristics of one important thing out of this complex, which thing is
interwoven with this complex and differentiates chorologically.
These geographic regions have been determined in their chorological extension in the same way as those of special geography,
although in the former the surface extension of the chorological
differentiations of *one* thing in its relation to the absolute extension of the surface of the ground is decisive.

General geography looks for that which is general in the chorological differentiation of the concrete earthly reality. It has to
ascertain the regularity in the chorological differentiation. Within
the infinite chorological differentiation it traces what is similar
in the differentiation of things, and tries to subsume them under
types and classes.

Before going further into the problems of general geography it
is necessary to say something about the difference between a
class and a type in general. We think we can circumscribe the
difference between a class and a type as follows: The characteristics
united in the conceptual content of a *class* can be applied completely

146

and in the same way to the members contained in the class. On the one hand classes can be subdivided by means of a division into sub-classes, and on the other hand classes can be included by means of a classification into super-classes. A *type* is a representative model, a pattern. The characteristics of the specimens of a type only approximately approach the characteristics united in the connotation of a type-concept. The specimens approach a type in different ways. There is some scope for variation. A type is sharply distinct in its nucleus only, whereas its outlines remain vague. The possibility of a classification of types is absent or very imperfectly realizable [19].

The process of the division of a class into sub-classes is called a *logical division;* the opposite process, viz., the inclusion of classes into higher classes is called *classification*. The result of a division, and that of a classification show the relations of the classes in the same way. The process of division proceeds from what is more general to that which is less general; that of classification proceeds from what is less general to what is more so. The former process reveals the difference between the sub-classes of a class; in the latter procedure that which is similar in the classes included in a super-class comes to the fore. This shows that classes and co-ordinate classes are distinguished by particular characteristics, but not by all their characteristics *. There are also common characteristics, and on the ground of these corresponding more general characteristics they are included in a higher, a more general class. In its turn the latter can be distinguished from co-ordinate classes, and on the ground of still more general characteristics these more general classes can be included into an even more general, higher class.

It will be clear that the arrangement of classes pre-supposes the knowledge of the characteristics of the various classes. This means that an extensive knowledge is required of individuals and individual phenomena that are subsumed under classes on the ground of some similar characteristics. This is previous to classi-

* Co-ordinate classes are the group of classes that form one and the same superclass, or originate from the division of one and the same superclass; in a wider sense they are all those classes that are on the same level of classification or division. We use the term here in its first sense.

147

fication and division. For classification and division are concerned with classes, classes of individuals and individual phenomena, but not with the individual things and individual phenomena themselves. As the experimental sciences have to start with the subsuming of individual things and phenomena under classes, it is obvious for them to try and accomplish a classification, and not immediately to start with a division from what is most general to what is least so *. But at some stage of such a classification the process of division will be important for verifying the process of classification.

In present day science logical division and classification are no aims in themselves. But, — and this is of the utmost importance to geography, — classification can be a means to grade the significance of the characteristics of the classes, and thus of the individual members of the classes. Geography deals with differences. The chorological differentiations are distinct from one another, but they do not differ in all their characteristics; there are also similar characteristics. By means of division and classification it is often possible to determine the significance of what is similar and of what is dissimilar.

The question is: Can we subsume the chorological differentiations of earthly objects and their phenomena under classes and divide and classify these classes?

It is certain that it is impossible to subsume the chorological differentiations under classes which can be grouped in a dichotomic division. In such a division the classes are always divided into two sub-classes, of which one possesses the characteristic of the division concerned and the other does not. But hardly any experimental science can use such divisions. As a rule co-ordinate classes are distinct from each other on account of characteristics that differ quantitatively, which are contiguous and pass into each other. In geography this occurs very frequently.

Geography, however, differs from many experimental sciences in

---

* In connection with the relation between a class and individual things (the members of a class) and that between a class and its sub-classes, we use the following terms: A class *contains* its members, an investigator *subsumes* individual things under a class, but a class *includes* its sub-classes and classes can be *included* into a higher class.

another respect. In such natural sciences as biology and geology genesis is very important. They lay emphasis on the genesis of individual things. Division and classification are determined by descent and genetic processes. If geography is conceived of as the total chorological differentiation of the earth surface in a particular length of time, especially in the time in which we live, genesis is not so essential (Chapter VI). Geography concentrates on the totality of the chorological differentiation. This means: although general geography in its search for what is general at first has to restrict itself to the general in the chorological differentiations of the *separate* earthly things, it does not stop there. In what is general it is the integration of the chorological differentiations of the separate things and phenomena that geography tries to find. General geography tries to integrate the types and the classes of these various differentiations. This principle of totality determines the inquiry into what is general in the separate things already at the outset. Those characteristics of a thing that differentiates chorologically are important, which are interrelated with the characteristics of other things that differentiate chorologically in a definite time.

Summarizing the above exposition we can establish the following: Geography is concerned with the chorological differentiation of a complex of things. These things are interwoven. Although these things influence each other, they do not all of them differentiate in a similar way; there is a semi-independent way of differentiating. Further, the genesis of separate things is mostly different. A genetic classification of the classes of separate things may be possible in many cases, but a genetic classification of the classes of the chorological differentiations of the entire complex of things is consequently impossible. However, this is not so essential to geography. Geography is concerned with the functional integration of things in their chorological diversity at a particular time. Chorological differentiations form regions. These regions, these chorological differentiants, contain the chorological differentiations of the whole complex, but these regions are determined in their *unity* according to particular important characteristics of one or a few things of that complex. Special geography determines this

149

unity according to an integration of a few things, general geography does so according to only one thing, although already at the outset the latter pays attention to those characteristics of this thing that are interrelated with the characteristics of other things. When general geography subsumes its regions under classes, the chorological differentiations of the whole complex of things has in reality been put together in classes on the ground of some important characteristics of one differentiating thing of that complex. For this one thing is interwoven in the complex of things. The regions subsumed under a class on the ground of common characteristics, are no individuals in the sense of the organisms subsumed under a class by biology. For the chorological differentiations of various things of the geographic complex in their chorological extension form a continuum, and in accordance with the question as to what characteristics of a thing are important for the chorological differentiation of that thing, the regions of the chorological differentiations will differ in extent and form.

If the opinion is held that a classification or a division should be genetic, we must say that geography cannot subsume the regions of a complex under classes, and cannot classify. Besides, we must establish then that geography as the science of the chorological differentiation of terrestrial reality in a particular time does not mean much and has little importance. For in this view genesis is not of primary importance. It is not the characteristics of the things that are fundamental for the genesis of the separate things that are important for geography, but the characteristics of the things that are essential to the integration of things at the time in which we live; and these characteristics are very often different from the former [20].

At the end of the preceding chapter we have explained that in our opinion the chorological differentiation of earthly reality in its functional vertical and horizontal integration at the present time is both important and meaningful. Although in this respect the course of development of the separate things may be important for a better understanding of the present earthly diversity, this genesis is not of decisive importance, nor is it a goal.

In another context Hartshorne also points out the meaning of "being" in its relation to "becoming" [21].

Schmitthenner, too, points out that it is impossible to conceive of regions as well-individualized spatial organisms (wohlindividualisierte Raumorganismen). Consequently it is impossible to accomplish a typification of part of what has been recognised as geographic material, or of the total content of the countries. ("Eine Typisierung aus dem gesamten als geographisch erkannten Material oder gar aus dem Gesamtinhalt der Länder, ist also nicht möglich"). General geography can only determine regions of a certain type on the ground of some particular characteristics of one thing out of a complex, says Schmitthenner. These types show some likeness to zoological types such as land animals and water animals; but they are no classes based on affinity and descent. Schmitthenner considers these types to be of little importance [22].

Land animals and water animals are no *genetic* classes [23], but are they no classes for this reason, and are these specific characteristics unimportant? Let us first consider the latter question. In our opinion the general concepts land- and water animals are of great importance from the viewpoint of geography. Hartshorne says that geography is a naive science, i.e., geography concentrates its attention on things and their integrations as they appear to us in reality [24]. In another context he demonstrates this with the following example: "To the geographer, as well as to the sailor, the whale is a fish or — if this be regarded as a misuse of a word — the whale is to be included under the general concept ocean animals rather than land animals" [25].

We would like to underline this statement. A geographer calls a whale a fish, because just like a fish a whale lives in the water, and is a water animal. The fact that a whale is a mammal and from this standpoint does not belong to the genetic class of fish, is of little importance to a geographer.

Hettner says: "The greatest difference on the earth surface is that between continent and sea. It is true, this difference is genetically speaking of a later date, it is secondary, ... But for the earth surface as the latter presents itself to our view, and on which organic life unfolds itself, this difference is more important than any

151

other distinction; whereas all other distinctions are made within some natural kingdom, this one is a distinction between the natural kingdoms themselves. All the relations of an anorganic as well as of an organic nature, and those of human life, are different on earth from those in the water" [26].

We have a strong impression that zoogeography takes little account of geographical problems. For although geography is a naive science, this naivety, too, has its own methodology. Most of the zoogeographers are zoologists, who approach zoogeography with the methods and concepts of zoology. As to the distinction between land animals and water animals, we cannot decide whether they are types or classes. To us there are classes if they can be systematized in a logical division. But in view of the great difference between land and water as environments, it seems quite possible to us to form sub-classes on the ground of the diversity within these environments. A whale lives in the oceans, and we might perhaps subdivide water animals into two sub-classes, viz., animals living in the oceans and those living in lakes and rivers, and the latter two classes can again be subdivided. The same thing will probably hold for the land animals which can be subdivided on the ground of their living in forests, grass lands and in other vegetable environments.

The generic concepts of most of the sciences are no universal concepts, but *collective generic concepts*. These concepts and the classes based on them and proceeding from them have been formed from a particular viewpoint according to particular common characteristics, which characteristics are essential from that standpoint. This abstraction views things from a particular angle; it is formal or quasi-partial, and not a total abstraction [27].

What principles lie at the foundation of a logical division? Stebbing [28] distinguishes three rules:
1. "There must be only one fundamentum divisionis at each step.
2. The co-ordinate classes must be collectively exhaustive of the super-class.
3. The successive steps of the division must proceed by gradual stages".

"It follows that co-ordinate classes must be mutually exclusive, . . . that every member contained in the classes is contained in one class only and no member in a superordinate class is omitted in the next level".

The first rule does not mean that the subordinate classes of one and the same super-class are to be divided in the same way. The various principles of division, however, must be interconnected with each other and with the original principle of division, or they must form a whole that is directed to a particular purpose.

As we have already observed in an earlier context, the experimental sciences must usually start with a classification that traces the process in the opposite direction. When we first consider the principles of classification, the method of comparison stands out clearly: Individual objects must first be subsumed under classes on the ground of similar characteristics. Even if there should be only types and no classes in geography, it would be necessary to compare similar chorological differentiations in order to determine types on the ground of common characteristics. However, we will posit the possibility of forming classes in geography. When these classes are included into super-classes it is done by means of the comparison of the classes according to common characteristics.

What is the purpose of ascertaining what is similar in general geography? Comparing individual chorological differentiations and subsuming them under a class means that they are stript of their accessory individual particularities and that the essential similar characteristics come to the fore. Similar chorological differentiations are abstracted in groups (classes) of chorological differentiations. These classes of chorological differentiations are distinct from each other, but they are not different in all their characteristics. On the ground of particular common characteristics that are more general and are determined by means of comparison, the various classes can again be included into super-classes. What is similar in particular classes constituting a super-class is again *distinct* from what is similar in other classes that are included in another super-class.

In a division we meet with the same relations, but the process is inverted. A class is divided into sub-classes, and the difference between these sub-classes comes to the fore. But in addition to the differences between the sub-classes of a class there are more general characteristics that are the same in these sub-classes, for on the ground of these more general common characteristics these sub-classes are included in that class.

The comparison of classes in a classification and in a division in order to ascertain the similarity and the difference between the classes is done in different phases and so on different levels. The division into primary classes is based on a primary principle of division; the division of these primary classes into subordinate classes is done on the basis of a less important principle of division. The further the division is continued the more the importance of the specific characteristics decreases. The lower classes possess all the characteristics of the higher classes from which they proceed. So the number of characteristics of the subordinate classes will continually increase, but the added characteristics will more and more decrease in significance. As a lower class can be expressed in terms of the higher classes from which it proceeds, and as the characteristics of the subordinate class are formed by the sum total of the characteristics of these higher classes, the division clearly shows the order of the characteristics of a class, and the different importance of the characteristics has been established. For, although the connotation (the characteristics) of every class forms a whole, a unity, the significance of one characteristic is greater than that of another.

It is clear that the connotation (the number of characteristics) of the higher classes will continually decrease, i.e., its definiteness will decrease [29]. In an ascending line the classes will become more and more general and fundamental. Classes resulting from the first division have only one characteristic, which has been determined by means of the specific characteristic (fundamentum divisionis) of the highest class (summum genus) [30]. The higher classes are consequently less definite and still imply all kinds of possibilities. For a higher class includes the lower classes in its extension.

The connotation of the higher class can be applied to its subordinate classes that are included by the higher class. This is why the connotation and the extension of concepts (classes) are inversely proportionate to each other [31]. The latter statement does not hold for the relation of a class to the members of that class. For the characteristics united in the connotation of a class are completely and similarly applicable to the members contained in that class. The number of members, therefore, does not determine the connotation of a class. Modern logic — unlike classical logic — distinguishes the relation of the individual objects and the class of which they are members from the relation of the sub-classes to the class including them.

In a classification we see the relations of the characteristics of the classes, and the relation of the connotation and the extension of a concept reflected in a direction which is opposite to that of a division. The common characteristics on the ground of which classes are included in a super-class will become more and more important and general, but the number of the characteristics of the super-classes will steadily decrease.

As has already been observed, geography, just like the experimental sciences generally, can work with a dichotomic division only with difficulty, because the objects contained in classes are often differentiated by the possession of a different quantity of a characteristic. It may occur that at a certain stage a division is dichotomic, so that a class includes two sub-classes of which the one possesses the specific characteristic and the other does not. At another stage of this division a class must often be subdivided into more than two sub-classes, as these sub-classes possess quantitatively different degrees of the specific characteristic [32]. When we consider the nature of the characteristics of the classes, we must remember that we are concerned with positive characteristics [33]. This means that in case of a further division of a class lacking the positive characteristic (which, consequently, is itself the result of a dichotomic division) one should be mindful of the positive meaning proceeding from a negative characteristic. When we divide soils into humid and non-humid soils, the latter term designates the positive properties of the absence of humidity (aridity). These non-humid soils (arid soils) are pedocals, calcareous (limy) soils. On the ground

155

of this characteristic these non-humid (arid) soils are subdivided into gray desert soils, brown steppe soils and chernozems.

General geography analyses and systematizes the chorological differentiations and their specific characteristics. Properly speaking, the former method is a means to the latter, which is the real goal: to establish the order of the significance of the characteristics forming a unity.

Special geography has to work with this conceptual material in order to determine the difference between the chorological differentiations of an integration of a few things out of the complex in a particular area of the world. Then, too, comparison is necessary for the ascertainment of the difference, the chorological differentiation. As in this case the issue is no longer the comparison of the general characteristics that many differentiations have in common, but the distinction between a few contiguous chorological differentiations, the investigation can extend to the unity of some interrelated chorological differentiations or an integration. Special geography is at once directed to the difference between the chorological differentiations, to the difference in the details of the complex. But in order to make a more detailed distinction between the chorological differentiation, special geography searches for unities within this complex. In our conception these unities are unities of totality that have been determined beforehand out of the complex of an area of the earth surface that is being investigated (Chapter III). The spatial extension, and in particular the surface extension of the chorological differentiation of such a totality or integration, constitutes the geographic region, the absolute extension of the ground being the fixed datum here. In general geography it is the surface extension of the chorological differentiation of one thing which, together with the ground, determines the region.

Also Schmitthenner points out this similarity between general geography and "Länderkunde" (special geography). In both of them "the regions have been determined according to a principle of construction. Regions have not been given, but they have been formed by us". He speaks of composition according to factors concerned with things ("Setzung nach sachlichen Faktoren") [34].

We, therefore, prefer the designation of special geography to that of regional geography, because the latter term suggests that in contra-distinction to general geography, only this geography has to do with regions.

It is clear that the objects that geography wants to classify differ widely from the individuals of a biological class. In its classification geography will consider the chorological differentiations of the earthly complex according to one thing out of the complex, and will mostly leave the internal and the external horizontal inter-connections out of the account. Everything is vertically inter-woven with other things of the complex to a greater or less degree. The regions formed out of a complex on the ground of the choro-logical differentiation of one thing in it, and placed in classes, vary in extent and form in dependence on the different character-istics of that thing. They will change again, if the characteristics of other things of the complex are used as a basis. Regions are, therefore, no independent individuals. The chorological differen-tiations of many things have no separate existence in their choro-logical extension, but pass into each other, forming a continuum such as soils, vegetations, and climates. As a result of this continuum there is usually also continuity and a certain decline of the character-istics of these chorological differentiations. There is some kind of similarity on this point with the phenomena belonging to a type. We repeat that there is some scope for variation in this case. A type is only sharply distinct in its nucleus, and its outlines are vague. The chorological differentiations often differ only quantita-tively from a particular characteristic, and they often vary within certain limits (e.g., climates). Near a limit there is little difference on either side, and on the ground of this limit we, nevertheless, think of two different differentiations brought under different classes. There are, however, also chorological differentiations that can be distinguished more sharply, such as forest and grass vegeta-tion, but here, too, there is a certain continuity in the vegetation which forms transitions. Classification in biology also has its difficulties, although they are less great. Stebbing quotes Goodrich as follows: "It is the universal experience of naturalists engaged in the classification of quite modern closely allied "species" that the

157

great difficulty of the work is due to the fact that it is usually scarcely possible to find any character at all sufficiently conspicuous and constant to distinguish them from each other" ... [35].

Although there is some similarity to a type, we are of the opinion that to a limited degree it is possible to subsume the chorological differentiations of earthly things under classes and to classify them. We base this idea on the fact that various characteristics — which recur all over the world — possess a certain hierarchical order of succession. This hierarchy suggests the possibility of classification. Stebbing observes that the main thing is to reach the *purpose* of the classification. This purpose is: "namely so to arrange classes that their relations may be exhibited in accordance with the principles of hierarchial order [36]".

Division and classification are no goal as such for us, but the means to determine the similarity and the difference between the characteristics of the chorological differentiations and to ascertain the order of the importance of these characteristics. The latter is hardly, or not at all, possible with types.

As the chorological differentiation of terrestrial objects results in regions, these regions are in a certain sense members of classes. But a strong restriction should be made here. In reality a region contains the extension of a complex of things which is more or less a chorological differentiant. A geographic region is only a unity according to a few characteristics of the differentiation of one thing in interrelation with the characteristics of the differentiations of some other things of the complex. But this thing and these few other interrelated things are interwoven with the remaining things of the complex. On the basis of this fact it is possible in a certain sense to consider the whole complex of things of a region in accordance with these characteristics of the differentiation of that one thing in interrelation with a few other things. Only on the ground of this limited unity is a region a member of a class. As a matter of fact, a region is also a specimen of a type only according to some characteristics of a thing out of the complex.

Classification will have to be directed to the chorological differentiation of one thing in connection with a few other things of the complex. We now wish to investigate further in what way the

158

hierarchical order of the characteristics comes to the fore in this case.

We will try to divide the world into classes of regions on the ground of the chorological differentiation of the atmospheric condition. The latter exerts a great influence on vegetation, on the soils, drainage and minor landforms. So, if the right characteristics are chosen for the determination of the various climates, the resulting climatic regions will not be isolated: in broad outlines these regions will also form vegetation regions and soil regions *.

What characteristics of the atmosphere are significant in this connection? Thornthwaite thinks that the elements of temperature and humidity are decisive in this case. The important thing is whether a climate is warm or cold, humid or dry. Thornthwaite [37] has composed two climatic classifications. Although the second is characterized by an improved technique as to the calculation of humidity, we shall restrict ourselves to his first study. It is concerned with the relation of the climate with natural vegetation, with the soils, and partly with drainage and the minor landforms. So it is concerned with the totality of the differentiations, and is essentially of a geographic character. In the second study the climate is considered as such, apart from its significance to the other things of the earthly complex [38]. There is perhaps some exaggeration in saying that the first classification is directed to the interrelation with vegetation, the soils, etc. Thornthwaite wants to classify the climates, and to ascertain the boundaries of the climatic regions he looks at the boundaries of the vegetation regions, etc., because the latter are closely connected with the former, and to a large extent, determined by them. This connection is rather a means to an end with Thornthwaite.

So Thornthwaite operates with humidity and temperature. Humidity or the effect of precipitation is determined by the quotient of the amount of precipitation and evaporation; this is the P-E ratio. The sum of the twelve monthly P-E ratios is the P-E index. Temperature efficiency is expressed in the T-E ratio, and the sum of the twelve monthly T-E ratios is the T-E index.

* For what follows we wish also to refer to our short study: De geografische classificatie van het klimaat en Thornthwaite's klimaatsystemen. Tijdschrift voor Economische en Sociale Geografie, Jrg. 48, 1957, afl. 1.

Thornthwaite sees humidity and temperature especially in connection with vegetation. According to him vegetation will increase with a rising degree of humidity, and also with a rising temperature up to a definite limit (ca. 86⁰ F.). The P-E index and the T-E index are equivalent and can be connoted and compared by means of the same magnitudes. Both indices are mutually related with respect to vegetation [39].

Then Thornthwaite arrives at the following types:

Types	P-E Index	Types	T-E Index
A (wet)	128 and higher	A' (tropical)	128 and higher
B (humid)	64—127	B' (mesothermal)	64—127
C (sub-humid)	32—63	C' (microthermal)	32—63
D (semi-arid)	16—31	D' (taiga)	16—31
E (arid)	0—15	E' (tundra)	1—15
		F' (perpetual frost)	0

The relation between humidity and temperature is indicated by Thornthwaite as follows: "Precipitation-effectiveness and temperature-efficiency are the two most significant climatic elements, and the relative importance of each depends upon its limiting effect. Where temperature-efficiency is adequate, variations in precipitation-effectiveness establish the primary climatic boundaries: otherwise temperature-efficiency is the limiting factor and determines the boundaries. If the temperature-efficiency index is less than 32, it controls the climate; if the index is more than 32, the climate is controlled by precipitation-effectiveness" [40].

He then distinguishes eight primary types: A, B, C, D, and E, with a T-E index of more than 32, and D', E', F' with a T-E index of less than 32.

The primary types A, B, C, D, E can be further subdivided by a variation of sufficient annual temperature-efficiency. The primary types D', E', F' are not further subdivided by a variation of precipitation-effectiveness, because according to Thornthwaite the latter is of little importance.

We must, however, bear in mind that precipitation and temper-

T-E index

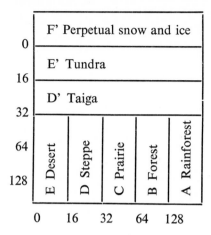

P-E index

ature do not differentiate in the same way. As humidity is determined by precipitation and evaporation, and the latter is chiefly
dependent on temperature, the chorological differentiations of
precipitation-effectiveness (humidity) and temperature-efficiency
will show less difference than those of precipitation and temperature.
But the difference is sufficiently great for the essential chorological
differentiations of the P-E and the T-E indices to overlap each
other.

For a further determination of types Thornthwaite distinguishes
variations of humidity in the seasons and the summer concentration
of temperature-efficiency. The characteristics concerning the annual
precipitation- and temperature-effectiveness are of primary importance in Thornthwaite's system. It might be asked, however,
in how far particular situations and variations of the seasons are
of a decisive significance with reference to the growth of natural
vegetation. In this connection we would refer to Hartshorne's
observation [41] about particular climatic types in Koeppen's system.
Here, however, we base ourselves on Thornthwaite's view, and as
we only want to examine in broad outlines in how far these types
can be used as classes, we restrict ourselves to the characteristics

161

of the P-E index and the T-E index, and leave the seasonal variations out of account.

Before making an effort to include these types in classes and to divide them, we will consider Thornthwaite's system in some more detail. With the exception of F' the types show their interrelation with variations of natural vegetation. F' does not possess any vegetation, is not a vegetation type, but it is a climatic type.

For the rest natural vegetation is a factor that cannot be used in many regions of the earth, as this vegetation is absent there and has been replaced by cultivated crops. The connection between variations of climate and variations of cultivated crops, however, differs from that between climate and natural vegetation. Thornthwaite, however, also uses the soils to determine climatic regions, although on some points the latter deviate from the climatic regions in relation with natural vegetation. But in connection with the cultivated crops and human tillage these soils are no longer in such a condition as the one in which they would be, if the climate alone exerted its influence on them. Such difficulties, of course, will show less, if the attempt is made to divide the whole world into a few large regions. In the case of a finer division, however, these drawbacks entail insurmountable difficulties. As Thornthwaite's division of the P-E and the T-E index, however, comprises very large regions, we shall assume for convenience' sake, that the above-mentioned objections are not too serious.

Thornthwaite makes a sharp distinction between warm and cold climates, between climates with sufficient and those with insufficient temperature-efficiency in connection with natural vegetation. He does not do so with respect to precipitation-effectiveness. He distinguishes five grades of precipitation-effectiveness, but he does not distinghuish them into humid and dry climates, or climates with sufficient and those with insufficient precipitation-effectiveness. In his system of climates and soils he does distinguish them. He divides the climates with a T-E index larger than 32 into two groups, viz., into humid and dry climates in accordance with humid and dry soils, viz., pedalfers and pedocals, in which the P-E index 48 forms the boundary [42].

As to the climates in relation with the variations of natural vegetation we, too, would consider this P-E index of 48 to be the boundary line between drier and more humid climates. The types C and D are then enclosed within the limits P-E 48—63 and P-E 16—47 *. To a certain extent we can speak of sufficient and insufficient annual humidity for the growth of natural vegetation.

Finally we must examine the structure of Thornthwaite's types a little in more detail. At first he speaks of the primary types A, B, C, D, E, and D', E', F', but later on he deviates from this series. After subdividing the first five primary types via a variation of sufficient annual temperature-efficiency, he arranges these fifteen types, viz., AA', AB', AC', and BA', BB', BC', etc., in one series on the same level with D', E', F'. This does not seem to be correct to us.

The types of the first group have two characteristics each, and the three types of the second group have one characteristic each, the latter characteristic being of a different kind from the principal characteristic of each of the types of the first group.

When we try to form classes from Thornthwaite's types of climate and to subject these classes to a process of division, we shall start from Thornthwaite's original types proceeding from the division of the P-E index and the T-E index. They were A, B, C, D, E, and A', B', C', D', E' and F'. As our division will be based on these types (classes), we will also maintain these indications, these terms, for clearness' sake.

---

* So we split up Thornthwaite's type C into two parts, viz., into a drier and a more humid part. We combine the drier part with type D to form class D with ampler limits. The more humid part of type C then becomes class C with narrower limits. The vegetation of class D consists of dry steppe grasses. The vegetation of class C consists of more humid grasses, prairiegrass.

For the further subdivision of the climates in relation to vegetation we maintain Thornthwaite's limits. On certain points this subdivision deviates from that of the climates in relation to soils, as Thornthwaite indicates. This is quite understandable, as they do not vary in a perfectly similar way.

We do not think that determining the boundary of the drier and of the more humid climates at P-E 48, and that of the warmer and the colder climates at T-E 32, is a contradictory practice. For although himidity and warmth are factors of the same value with respect to the growth of natural vegetation, they will not be perfectly proportionate. This already appears from the fact that according to Thornthwaite growth no longer increases above 86° F., whereas with regard to humidity no limit has apparently been fixed.

163

We would carry out the following division:

T-E index

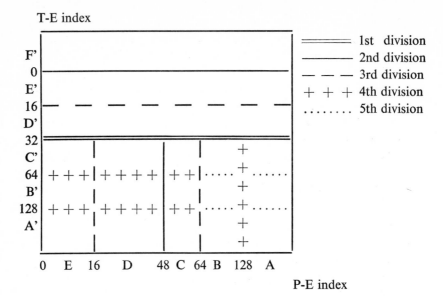

1st division
2nd division
3rd division
+ + + 4th division
.... 5th division

P-E index

1st Division: The division of the summum genus, the earthly climate, into two primary classes. The principle of division (fundamentum divisionis) is the difference in temperature-efficiency.

I   D' E' F' as a whole *, insufficient warmth, colder climates.
II   A' B' C' as a whole, sufficient warmth, warmer climates.

If two primary classes are formed, the principle of division on which this division is based must be more fundamental than the following principles of division in the later sub-divisions. As these climates are related with natural vegetation, the difference between the vegetations of warmer and colder climates must be more fundamental than the difference between the vegetations of the regions appearing in the sub-divisions. According to Bengtson and Van Royen the difference between warmer and colder climates is primary, and of more essential importance for the difference in the

* D' E' F' as a whole means that this primary class possesses the essential common characteristic of its including classes. This characteristic of insufficient temperature-efficiency is bounded by the limits 0 and 31 of the T-E index.

kinds of plants than the distinction of humid and dry climates [43]. This is a difficult point, for Thornthwaite's system speaks of natural vegetation, and this is something different from a plant-species. Besides, he also speaks of effectiveness and efficiency for the growth of vegetation. He is, therefore, concerned with the quantity and the differentiation of vegetations. We cannot judge of this matter. If the difference in vegetation is really fundamental, there are two primary classes. If the difference is not so great as the distinctions in a sub-division, we shall have to consider these two as separate groups of climates, which cannot be mutually compared, and which require two divisions. This, however, does not affect the nature of a further division. Let us here stick to one summum genus of which the colder and the warmer climates are the two principal classes *.

2nd Division: The division of the primary classes.

D' E' F' as a whole is divided into two classes according to a difference in insufficient temperature-efficiency: D' E' as a whole, slight temperature-efficiency and F' no temperature-efficiency. The former has a scarce vegetation, the latter has no vegetation.

A' B' C' as a whole is divided according to a difference in pre-cipitation-effectiveness into two classes: A B C as a whole, sufficient humidity and D E as a whole, insufficient humidity.

3rd Division: The division of the classes.

D' E' as a whole is divided according to a difference in a low degree of warmth into two subordinate classes: D' taïga and E' tundra.

A B C as a whole is divided in accordance with a difference in sufficient humidity into two subordinate classes: A B as a whole, a high degree of humidity and C a moderate degree of humidity. This division is revealed in a difference of vegetation, viz., forest and grass land.

D E as a whole is divided according to a difference in insufficient

* In our first study of Thornthwaite's climatic types we distinguished two separate groups of climates and two different divisions. Then we based ourselves on the supposition that the difference between the vegetations of the colder and the warmer climates is perhaps not so fundamental as the difference of the vegetations of particular climates in the sub-division, e.g., the vegetations of A and E within the warmer climates.

humidity into two subordinate classes: D a low degree of humidity (steppe) and E a very low degree of humidity (desert shrub).

4th Division: The division of the subordinate classes.

A B as a whole is divided according to a difference in a high degree of humidity into two sub-classes: A the highest degree of humidity (rainforest) and B a higher degree of humidity (forest).

C is divided according to a difference in sufficient warmth into three sub-classes: C A' the highest degree of warmth, C B' a higher degree of warmth, and C C' a moderate degree of warmth.

D is divided according to a difference in sufficient warmth into three sub-classes: D A', D B' and D C'.

E is divided according to a difference in sufficient warmth into three sub-classes: E A', E B', and E C' *.

5th Division: The division of the sub-classes.

A is divided according to a difference in sufficient warmth into three subordinate sub-classes: A A', A B', and A C'.

B is divided into three subordinate sub-classes according to a difference in sufficient warmth: B A', B B', and B C'.

The vegetation of the sub-classes and the subordinate sub-classes can easily be deduced. E.g., A A' a very warm rain-forest; A B' a warm rain-forest, A C' a moderately warm rain-forest.

We speak of first, second division, etc. But every division consists of various divisions; they belong, however, to the same level: the level of the first division, of the second division, etc. The various divisions of the same level often have different principles of division. This is permissible, but the principle of division of one and the same division, of one class must not be changed. The principles

---

* The division of the classes of *insufficient humidity* (D and E) according to a differentiation of sufficient warmth might raise the question as to whether this division really corresponds with natural vegetation classes that are essentially different, as is certainly the case with the division of the sub-classes of *sufficient humidity*, e. g., A according to the variation of sufficient warmth. The problem arises as to whether the differentiation of warmth is still important in the case of climates with insufficient humidity. Is there a restriction to be made here similar to the one that holds for climates with *insufficient* warmth (D', E', and F') in which the differentiation of humidity is of little importance? Thornthwaite affirms the latter, but he does not posit the former problem. At least, he simply divides D and E in the same way as A according to the variation of sufficient warmth.

of division of one and the same level and those of the various levels of division, however, should be interconnected. Our division meets these requirements: The principles of division consist in gradations of warmth and humidity. These characteristics are both essential to a climate, and for a great part they are equivalent and proportionate to natural vegetation and show their mutual relationship in this respect. In these specific characteristics sufficient or insufficient warmth functions as a primary principle of division.

The level of a division is very important because it indicates the order of the significance of the characteristics. The characteristics of the second division are more important than those of the third division, etc. As the subordinate classes possess the characteristics of the super-classes from which they proceed, the order of the characteristics of every class can be determined. Then by means of a comparison of the various classes we can establish which of their characteristics in their order of significance are similar and which are different. On this ground the nature of the difference between the classes can be ascertained, for this *difference* is of the utmost importance. These distinctive characteristics can be attributed to the regions, to the chorological differentiants that are members of the various classes.

When, e.g., we examine the subordinate sub-class A A' more closely, we see that it can be expressed in terms of A, of A B, of A B C and of A' B' C' *, just like the subordinate sub-classes A B' and A C'. Together with the two other subordinate sub-classes, A A' possesses the characteristics of the four super-classes from which they proceed, viz., the highest degree of humidity, a high degree of humidity, sufficient humidity and sufficient warmth. The three subordinate sub-classes are only differentiated by a variation of sufficient warmth. A A' possesses the highest degree of warmth. The order of succession of the characteristics shows that the more special characteristics lend greater definiteness to a subordinate sub-class. The greatest warmth and the highest degree of humidity are a further definition of a sufficiency of warmth and a sufficient and high degree of humidity.

* The indication "as a whole" used with reference to the last three classes in an earlier context for clearness' sake, will be omitted in what follows.

167

We should not exclusively consider what is special and what is more definite in a characteristic. In the case of such a characteristic as "highest" degree of humidity the word "highest" is not the only one that is important. It is important if A A' is distinguished from B A', which latter class does not possess the highest degree but a higher degree of humidity. The characteristic "highest degree of humidity", however, implies the more general characteristic of a high degree of humidity. The latter characteristic determines class A B, in which A A' is included, and which characteristic is, consequently, also found in A A'. This characteristic of a high degree of humidity is very significant as compared with and in its difference from the moderate degree of humidity of C, if we pay attention to the difference in vegetation of forest and humid grassland. Also the difference in soil comes to the fore: humid forest soil and prairy soil. But however important this difference may be, what is similar in the characteristics of A B and C, viz., sufficient humidity, is even more fundamental. The importance of this characteristic of A B C is evident if this characteristic is seen in its *difference* from the insufficient humidity of D E. This also appears from the difference in vegetation and in soil, viz., humid grass-land, forest vegetation * and pedalfers, over against dry steppe vegetation, desert shrub and pedocals. This characteristic of A B C is also a characteristic of A A' which proceeds from this class. The general characteristic of sufficient humidity by which A A' is distinct e.g., from the general characteristic of insufficient humidity of D A' ** is more fundamental than the characteristic of the highest degree of humidity which distinguishes A A' from the higher degree of humidity of B A'. The same thing holds for the respective differences in vegetation: the difference between forest — humid grass

---

* Then humid grass land and forest are not considered in their difference, but what is similar in these two forms of vegetation will be brought to the fore in its difference from the dry steppe vegetation and from desert shrub. The issue, therefore, is concerned with humid grass and forest as a whole, over against steppe vegetation and desert shrub as a whole.

** Of course, A A' and D A' are also distinguished from each other by a difference in humidity that has been further defined, but this question is not the issue here. Here we are concerned with the more general difference in humidity.

as a whole and dry steppe vegetation — desert shrub as a whole is more fundamental than the difference between rainforest and forest. The difference is also more essential in the case of the soils: the difference between pedalfers and pedocals is more fundamental than the difference between a yellow red laterite soil and a brown red laterite soil, which latter are only a further distinction within pedalfers.

The difference in importance between the characteristics also tells us something else. The various classes formed by means of the gradations of the P-E and the T-E index and by their combinations are essential uniform differentiations. Especially vegetation and the soil show this. The subordinate class C is bounded by the limits P-E 48 and P-E 63, and is characterized by humid grass and prairie soil. Every region with a P-E index within these limits e.g., 51—59, belongs to this lower class C and has this vegetation and this soil. Then a region with the limits P-E 57—71 is not an essential climatic differentiation; its vegetation is partly grass and partly forest, and in one part the soil is a prairie soil and in the other part it is a forest soil. This region belongs neither to class C nor to class B, but to both. However, the matter is not so simple as that: It can be rightly said that a region with a P-E index of 57—71 is indeed an essential chorological differentiation and certainly belongs to an important class. For this region falls within the P-E index 48—128 and higher, and belongs to the higher class A B C with sufficient humidity, with humid grass and forest vegetation, and with a soil belonging to the pedalfers. Viewed from the standpoint of these important fundamental characteristics, the region bounded by the limits P-E 57 and P-E 71 is undoubtedly an essential chorological differentiation. It all depends on the question as to what characteristics will be used as a basis for the determination of the essential chorological differentiation, the more general or the less general characteristics, the latter of which make the region more definite. According to the former characteristics this region is an essential chorological differentiation, but according to the latter characteristics it is not an essential chorological differentiation. Yet there is a restriction to be made in connection with this explanation. A region bounded by the P-E index 57—71 will often not be distinct from the immediately adjoining regions. The latter will also as a rule belong to class A B C as a whole with sufficient humidity. With respect to these regions the region under discussion is not an essential chorological differentiant. It would be one with respect to regions with insufficient humidity belonging to class D E as a whole possessing steppe vegetation and desert shrub and soils of the class of the pedocals. These regions are generally not contiguous with the region in question.

The same thing is applicable to an arable and a dairy-farming region. A region possessing arable farms in one half and dairy farms in the other half, is not an essential chorological differentiant from the point of view of a further distinction of arable farming and dairy-farming; it is an undoubted essential chorological differentiant from a viewpoint which distinguishes agriculture from manufacturing industry. The more general and fundamental characteristics of what is agrarian belong to this region. Here, too, the same restriction holds as the one that applies to the climatic region just mentioned.

The above exposition shows that the members of a geographic class are no individuals in the sense of the members of a biological class. When we study Thornthwaite's [44] climatic map of the world, we see that the Central Congo region belongs to the lower sub-class B A', the Eastern Congo region belongs to the lower sub-class B B'. If we look upon these two adjoining regions as a whole, this larger region belongs to the higher class (in our division the sub-class) B. This shows clearly that the members of a geographic class are no individuals, for individuals cannot be combined into another and larger individual.

This map of the world also teaches us something else. The larger Congo-region we have discussed, belongs to the sub-class B. It consists of two adjoining regions: the one belongs to the lower sub-class B A', and the other to that of B B'. But a region of the lower sub-class B C' that would be contiguous with either of the two regions mentioned is not to be found there. This is to say: A larger region in Central Africa belonging to sub-class B, which would consist of three parts, which would each of them be members of all three lower sub-classes of the sub-class B respectively,

170

does not exist. On Thornthwaite's map of the world we have found only one such larger region of the sub-class B: this is the long drawn out region along the East coast of North America. Also of the larger regions belonging to the sub-classes A, C, D and E respectively, there is hardly any one or none at all to be found consisting of three adjoining regions which belong to the respective lower sub-classes A', B', and C'.

It is not so difficult to find the cause. Let us again think of sub-class B. This is bounded by the limits P-E 64 and 127. The limits of C', B', and A' are bounded by T-E 32—63, 64—127 and 128—± 180. A region that would contain three regional parts belonging to the lower sub-classes C', B', and A', would have to embrace a comprehensive margin of the T-E index, e.g., T-E- 50—150. It is obvious that B, determined within the narrower limits does not possess within its boundaries e.g., P-E 70—90, the comprehensive margin of T-E 50—150 which would encompass the three regional parts belonging to C', B' and A'. We must add something to this: the classes have been formed in accordance with precipitation-effectiveness and temperature-efficiency. The former is determined by the quantity of the precipitation and by evaporation. Evaporation is chiefly dependent on temperature. Precipitation-effectiveness or humidity is consequently determined for a considerable part by precipitation. Temperature-efficiency is exclusively formed by temperature. As precipitation and temperature do not chorologically differentiate alike, a region, determined according to an essential differentiation of narrower limits of humidity, will have fewer possibilities of a number of essential differentiations of temperature which are found together within the limits of a much larger distance. But, — we may say — B not only has the characteristic of a higher degree of humidity, e.g., P-E 70—90, it also has the characteristic of sufficient warmth, and the latter is determined by the limits 32 and ± 180. True, but this does not mean that this large margin is indispensable. Any margin, however small, answers the requirement of sufficient warmth, provided the latter lies within the T-E index of 32—± 180, or rather: if it lies above the T-E index 32.

The classes we have formed strongly resemble types. Up to

a certain limit of the P-E index, or of the T-E index, we have to do with this class, and when this limit is exceeded, we speak of another class. Class B (a sub-class in our division) is bounded by the limits 64 and 127 of the P-E index. With a P-E index of 62 and 129 we already find ourselves in the classes C and A. If we assign the characteristic of a higher degree of humidity to B as compared with C and A, which possess a moderate and the highest degree of humidity, it will be clear that this higher degree of humidity is most marked in the case of a P-E index within B lying at a good distance from the two limits mentioned. Individual regions, belonging to class B, will, therefore, be characterized more or less strongly by a higher degree of humidity in dependence on the distance between the P-E indices and the limits of B. This strongly resembles a type. Its nucleus is sharp, its edges are vague *.

The climatic types or classes we have formed, however, conform to a logical division and classification. There is a distinct hierarchy and order of climates. This is why we prefer the term class. The individual regions belong to particular classes on the ground of particular characteristics. In a figurative sense these regions are members of these classes. A class is not a region itself, and no matter how far the division would be continued, we should always obtain lower sub-classes, but no individual regions.

All the climatic classes we have formed from Thornthwaite's

---

* Many classes can be said to show some resemblance to a type. When we divide university students at the end of their study according to the result of their study, we can distinguish two classes: that of the successful students and that of the unsuccessful students. These classes are entirely based on the principle of division of a sufficient or an insufficient performance. A few students whose performances differ only slightly do not belong to the same class, however. They are the students with a barely sufficient performance, and those with a slightly insufficient performance. The fundamentum divisionis of a sufficient or an insufficient performance is vague in its line of demarcation. But the specific characteristic leads to a dichotomic division into two classes that exclude each other completely: successful and unsuccessful students.

The comparison of students with climates is, of course, imperfect in some respects. The slight difference between climates with barely sufficient and those with slightly insufficient humidity is probably also slight in its effect. The slight difference between a barely sufficient and a slightly insufficient performance of students, on the other hand, is much greater in its effect of successful and unsuccessful candidates.

system have members; there are no empty classes among them. A super-class has a smaller number of characteristics than its sub-classes, but indirectly a super-class contains more members (regions): Class B contains the regions of the sub-class B A' as well as those of the sub-classes B B' and B C'. When two regions of coordinate classes are contiguous, they can be united into a larger region which is a direct member of the super-class. This region as a member of that super-class has a larger extension, but a smaller number of characteristics than the component parts as members of the subordinate classes: The Congo region belongs to class B, and as a member of that class it has fewer characteristics than its two regional parts that are members of the sub-classes B A' and B B'. This shows that a region as a member of a class and according to the characteristics of that class is not an independent individual thing. In addition we can say that a region as a member of a class possesses all the relevant characteristics of that class in all its parts. That is to say a region as a member of a class is determined according to characteristics in uniform chorological extension.

Thornthwaite's map of climates shows that the individual regions of a class lie scattered over the earth surface. These regions are determined in size and form according to the extension of the chorological differentiations of the atmosphere which have been formed according to these characteristics of the atmosphere.

It is clear that in this process the horizontal interconnections on the earth surface are broken through. On the ground of a few important characteristics, a particular region of the Eastern Hemisphere belongs to a definite class together with a particular region of the Western Hemisphere. The individual horizontal connections that each of these two regions possesses with respect to contiguous regions — which belong to other classes — are left out of account. The characteristics on account of which certain regions belong to that particular class, however, are very important, because they are interrelated with some characteristics of other things of those regions. These are vertical interrelations. The classes have, consequently, been determined according to the viewpoint of what is general, of what is similar in the vertical interrelations.

This general characteristic, however, often proceeds from individual horizontal interconnections. Hettner says: "Only those phenomena on earth are general that proceed from the differentiation of the great individual phenomena under different conditions and the analogous repetition of the differentiated parts under similar conditions, consequently, they cannot be understood at all without the great individual phenomena" [45]. Of this the individual climatic zones on earth are a clear illustration, in which especially the difference between land and sea, the interchange of high and low land, and the difference between the East and the West side of the continents on different latitudes, are very important. In how far these individual horizontal interconnections of the regions can be fitted into types is a difficult problem. But however important the particular horizontal interconnections may be for the formation of regions of a certain class, this class has not been defined in the above exposition according to characteristics of the horizontal interconnections, but they possess characteristics that are directed to vertical interrelations of the regions.

We have dwelt upon geographic classes of climates, vegetation and soils. These classes have a simple structure. The classification of economic and cultural phenomena would be a great deal more difficult. Hartshorne observes that in the formation of types and classes of economic life it is necessary to distinguish between the classification of agriculture, mining and industry, because these three methods of production have widely different relations with the ground and with the other things of nature. Hartshorne has made a division of agrarian land use which seems to us to be important, because it is an effort to arrange the principles of division into a distinct hierarchy [46]. In our opinion his division is more important in this respect than Whittlesey's [47]. The latter lays greater emphasis on the character than on the hierarchy of the significance of the principles of division. How difficult it is to draw up a logical division — or only types of economic life and methods of production — also appears from the studies by Hartshorne in cooperation with Dicken [48], and from the textbooks by Bengston and Van Royen [49], Boesch [50], and "Erde und Weltwirtschaft" [51], to mention only a few of this category.

Bengtson and Van Royen, Boesch and also Lütgens in part of the work mentioned just now use climatic types as a basis for types of agrarian regions. This has its great drawbacks, however, of which the authors are hardly or not at all aware. For in primitive agrarian regions the almost unchanged natural vegetation is the basis of production in many cases, but in modern regions cultivated crops are predominant. The relations of the variations of natural vegetation and cultivated crops with the variations of climate are not the same. An additional difficulty is that the relations of the different cultivated crops with the climate are again different. But generally we can say: A classification of the climate directed to the integration with a classification of cultivated crops will have to start with a primary division into two primary classes or two separate primary groups based on a difference in humidity. The fundamentum divisionis is that of sufficient or insufficient precipitation-effectiveness for the growth of cultivated crops. So there are two classes of climates (groups): humid and dry climates. The former must be subdivided according to a differentiation of temperature-efficiency, and the latter must be subdivided according to a differentiation of insufficient precipitation-effectiveness. This division is quite different from the one that is directed to the integration with natural vegetation that we have discussed in great detail in an earlier context. If we want to classify the agrarian regions of the world and subdivide them, it will immediately be necessary to make two separate divisions, one for the regions with natural vegetation, and one for those with cultivated crops.

There are, however, other difficulties as well. The significance of the soil to agrarian production is also widely different. In many regions fertility is of primary importance. This fertility depends on the texture and the structure, and on the chemical and organic composition of the soil. In other regions, such as modern regions, the form of the land is of decisive importance: the flatness and smoothness of the territory is of the highest importance for the efficient use of agricultural machinery. In certain cases it is a combination of characteristics of the first and the second group: for dry farming in the Great Plains both the fine texture (for keeping the scanty supply of rainwater) and the smoothness of the territory are very important. Not long ago in the regions of South China with their intensive cultivation of rice the combination of the fertility of the soil and the natural hollow of a valley within the territory, were highly important. If one considers that according to physical, chemical and organic characteristics and according to the outward shape — such as smoothness and unevenness — the soils do not differentiate chorologically in the same way, and therefore form different regions, the matter becomes even more complicated.

One division comprising classes of all the agrarian regions of the world is absolutely excluded. There will have to be made various separate divisions. Then the diversity of the level of technique and the difference in the social-economic order is of primary importance. In forming classes of economic geographic regions we shall have to start from what is economic and not from the climate or from any other factor of nature. The higher the technical level the less we speak of the determining effect of nature.

In their turn such classes and types are in the first place determined by general characteristics directed to the interrelation with the characteristics of other things in these regions, and, consequently, refer to the vertical interrelations. But also the horizontal interconnections of economic and cultural phenomena are partly capable of being subjected to a general comparative study. We are referring, e.g., to horticultural regions belonging to different types on the ground of their different relative locations with respect to the market and the outlets. Horticultural regions lying in the immediate vicinity of large centres of population and selling their products there, have a different structure and a different function from those of horticultural regions that produce for remote regions. Various characteristics — such as the kind of the products, that of storage, of trade and traffic — belong to two different types. This difference of the internal and external horizontal interconnections is, therefore, important in itself and for a distinction in the characteristics that are significant to the vertical interrelations in these regions. These characteristics can be brought under types and classes of characteristics directed to the vertical interrelations and under types directed to the horizontal interconnections [52]. In the case of the latter we prefer to speak of types. In our opinion it is extremely difficult to form a hierarchy of classes of differentiations of the horizontal interconnections based on a differentiation of their relative locations.

When we compare the regions of geographic classes of climate with those of social and cultural life, it mostly appears that a region belonging to a particular class of climate differs in extent and form from the region there which belongs to a particular class of social and cultural life. This again shows that a region as a unity is not an individual like a member of a biological class. A region as a unity is determined in its chorological extension according to some characteristics. If other characteristics are introduced as determining factors, we often obtain a different region.

The conceptions of the relation between general and special geography are widely different, and the name "regional geography", often used to indicate special geography, has contributed to the confusion. Wooldridge and East [53] point out that it would be better to maintain the old term "special geography"; we have argued the same point in the above exposition as well as in an earlier publication [54].

But we are of opinion that the relation between general and special geography is directly determined by the view of the nature of geography as such. In this connection the ideas of Bobek are significant. He says that geography is determined by its object [55]. Next the method of study is important: the latter may be idiographic or generalizing-nomothetic. In this way he distinguishes special (regional) geography, landscape geography and general or elementary geography (Länderkunde, Landschaftskunde, und Allgemeine oder Elementargeographie). The first of these investigates the whole complex of things and phenomena of a country which determines its unique nature (einmaliges Wesen), the view is idiographic. Landscape geography (Landschaftskunde) studies particular integrations (hochrangige Komplexe) of the whole complex. These objects lend themselves to a nomothetic view. General geography (Allgemeine Geographie) consists of various geographical sciences, such as geomorphology, climatology, economic geography, etc. They investigate only a few elements and complexes of elements; the view is nomothetic, generalizing [56].

Bobek apparently does not consider the geographic aspect to be decisive, for the idiographic and nomothetic views are no aspects. For if we see the geographic aspect in the principle of chorological differentiation, both the idiographic and the nomothetic views are ruled by this aspect. This is why Bobek does not arrive at a sharp demarcation of geography with respect to history. The historical process of change and growth is very important in his "Länder-kunde". According to Bobek the genetic process is of the highest importance in all the three fields of geographic investigation [57].

To our mind Bobek takes too little account of the fact that the characteristics of a thing which are of the greatest significance for the process of its genesis, are often less important for the function of this thing in its interrelation with other things of a region at the present time. Geography is concerned with the latter.

It has been greatly to the credit of Hartshorne that better than anyone else he saw that the functional integration of dissimilar things at the present time is more important to geography than the genetic processes of things. Hartshorne's principal work is ruled by this thought. This principle holds both for his special and for his general geography. With respect to the latter he says: "that type concepts based on genesis may have little significance for func-tion" [58]. "Generic concepts and systems of classification will there-fore be more useful in geography if based on the functional rather than the genetic aspects of phenomena" [59]. When he has discussed the significance of the types of landforms, he winds up saying: "In other words he (the geographer) is more concerned with the form or physiognomy of the landform as a functioning factor in the total complex of areal phenomena than as an end product of its own genetic causes" [60]. Hettner's standpoint is less clear. In his trend of thought, genesis is decisive [61]. In a few other places, how-ever, he speaks his mind in favour of the functional integration [62].

In this connection we should point out that Schaefer's [63] criticism of Hartshorne saying that the latter has an eye only for geography as a naive science which only produces idiographic concepts, is entirely wrong. Hartshorne has given an elaborate and thorough exposition of the significance of "generic concepts" of geography [64]. On the other hand Hartshorne has also pointed out the limits of the possibilities of these "generic concepts". As geography is concerned with the totality of the chorological differentiations, the possibility of discovering generic concepts is restricted. Separate things vary chorologically in a semi-independent way. There are no universal laws governing the total chorological differentiation. Hence the sharp distinction made by Hartshorne between systematic general geography and the systematic sciences of separate things and phenomena. The latter study things in their isolation and as such. In the systematic sciences the genetic process is essential. To general geography the genetic process is something secondary. For the genetic processes of various things are very often different and in many cases they are not decisive of the functional integration of the chorological differentiations of things at the present time.

We consider the generic concepts and classifications of general geography to be very important for a deeper insight into the chorological differentiation of the world. They may be useful to us for determining the order of the significance of the characteristics of the chorologically differentiated things and their regions. They are the basis on which our knowledge of the regions should rest. The important thing is the distinction of the regions. For the indication of a region is based on its difference from other, especially from adjoining regions.

Geography is concerned with the totality of the chorological differentiation at the present time. In order to determine the order of the significance of the characteristics of the chorological differentiations of a thing, it is necessary first to ascertain the interrelation of this thing with other things of the earthly complex. The importance of a thing for the various other things of the complex may vary greatly, and in addition the various characteristics of this thing in their importance for the characteristics of the other things may diverge strongly. General geography, therefore, should start from the chorological differentiations of one thing and then ascertain the influence of the chorological differentiations of other things on this one thing. General geography concentrates its attention on a particular unity of totality within the earthly complex: an economic-geographic, a politico-geographic, a pedological-geographic totality, etc. The characteristics of things of nature that are significant in an economic-geographic totality, are not always important, or of the same significance in a politico-geographic integration, and vice versa.

It is usually very difficult to say which unity of totality or integration within the whole complex is the most important. In Chapter III we have elaborately discussed the anthropocentric character of geography. The earthly complex is considered from the viewpoint that the earth is the habitation of man, that man is the most important inhabitant of the earth. The significance of an integration is, therefore, determined by the importance of the chorological differentiations of this integration for the chorological differentiations of the earthly complex, the latter of which are the various living-areas of the human inhabitants. This, too, is often difficult to establish. In Chapter II we have pointed out the great importance of the ground for all other things of the earthly complex, also for man. In our opinion the significance of an integration, of a unity of totality, must also be determined by the importance of the ground, the soil within such an integration.

So we lay the stress on the importance of a thing for some other things, or to put it more generally: we emphasize the functional integration of things within the entire earthly complex. According to some authors in this way geography will become a science of relations. Bobek [65], e.g., is of the opinion that, although unjustly, the chorological principle has driven geography into the waters of a science of relations (beziehungswissenschaftlichen Fahrwasser). This seems to be incorrect. Hartshorne says: "To insist that for phenomena to be geographically significant they must be causally interrelated with other regional phenomena, is not to define geography as the study of relationships; if we say that a house cannot be built of bricks without mortar, we are not saying that a house consists of mortar" [66].

Let us revert to general geography, however. As we have explained just now, general geography should concentrate its attention on a unity of totality. The different classifications primarily differ according to the nucleus of the various unities of totality.

In an economic-geographic totality the chorological differentiations of the nucleus, i.e., economic life, must first be classified. Next the chorological differentiations of other things, especially those of nature, which influence the chorological differentiations of economic life, must be classified. The second classification has its co-determinant in the first, because attention should be paid to those characteristics which are significant to the characteristics of the first classification. The first classification, however, also has its co-determinant in the second. For the emphasis is laid on those characteristics of economic life which are strongly influenced by the characteristics of nature and are interrelated with them. But it is necessary for this unity of totality, this integration, to be restricted to a few elements. Regularity and law can only be ascertained within a few integrated elements of some dissimilar chorologically differentiated things. The simpler an integration is, the greater the number of the examples of the chorological differentiation of the integrated things will probably be. At first we should restrict ourselves to two dissimilar things, to a nucleus and one more thing bearing on it. Not until the chorological differentiations of these two things, which are interrelated, have been placed in classes, and these classes have been fitted into a logical division, or into a classification, will it be possible to make an effort to relate more things to the nucleus, and to classify these things together with the nucleus, into a more complex integration.

As we have explained in great detail in an earlier context, it is perhaps possible to group particular elements of nature, such as the climate, natural vegetation, and the soils, more or less into one world-wide classification. This is impossible for cultural things in connection with those of nature. Even a simple cultural-geographic totality diverges over the earth surface. The simplest agrarian-geographic totality, such as the integration of agriculture based on vegetation, diverges: In proportion as natural vegetation or cultivated crops govern the economic life of the various areas, other characteristics of temperature and humidity of the climate will be significant to a logical division and a classification. In the case of a higher level of economic life the matter is a great deal more difficult. The socio-economic order, the density of the population (intensive and extensive land use) and technique give rise to great differences in the significance of the characteristics of the soils, both as regards their chemical composition and their physical condition of texture and structure, while the characteristics of the landform cross the significance of the former characteristics. This is why it is necessary to divide the world into unities with a certain degree of homogeneity of culture and technique. Within every part there will then be a certain similarity of the importance of the characteristics of particular chorologically differentiating elements of nature for the characteristics of the chorological differentiations of economic life. Thus classifications and generic concepts are obtained which are only valid for particular parts of the world. These classifications are based on the functional integration at the present time and not on the genesis of things. To our mind Krebs's monumental work "Vergleichende Länderkunde" [67], especially as regards its general part, takes this too little into account.

The knowledge of the general chorological differentiations of the world is indispensable to gaining knowledge of the characteristics of the particular chorological differentiations of a part of the world and to the indication of one region in its difference from the surrounding regions. Some knowledge of general geography is required for the study of special geography. General geography, however, also has a right of its own to exist. For there is a need to gain an insight into the chorological differentiation of the world in its entirety, in which the issue is the chorological differentiation in broad outlines resulting in large regions.

Special geography uses generic concepts and the relations of these generic concepts. But general geography has to start from individual members when determining classes, and will, therefore, draw on the results of the special-geographic investigations of many regions.

If we want to determine the chorological differentiation of a part of the world by means of an *individual* division, it is important to base it on a definite unity of totality. If we should use elements that possess little interrelation, the division would result in regions that cannot be indicated and distinguished in an essential way, because the characteristics of the regions do not form a unity and the order of the significance of the characteristics is difficult to ascertain. Besides the regions will be more difficult to establish in their chorological extension and mutual boundaries: If we should begin with a division according to the structure of the ground, and afterwards make a further division according to climates, we should remember that these two elements differentiate chorologically in different ways. The regions of the first division, which show a certain degree of unity in their internal structure and composition of the ground, are not regions with a certain amount of unity and uniformity of climate. It would entail great difficulties if we should try to subdivide regions that do not conform to the chorological extension of climatic regions, into various smaller regions, each approaching to a certain unity of climate. This kind of difficulty is essentially the same for every part of the world that we wish to divide. This is why the chorological extension of the area that is to be divided should be determined beforehand in accordance with the chorological extension of the unity of totality that is to function as the basis of the division.

If, e.g., we concentrate on an economic-geographic totality of integration, economic life will be the nucleus of the entire division, and of the whole of the chorological differentiation of that part of the world. In the first division we choose a very simple integration, in which there is great similarity between the chorological differentiation of important economic phenomena and the chorological differentiation of the phenomena of another thing of the earthly complex. Then we arrive at a number of regions, each of which forms a certain unity according to that integration. Each region is distinct from its *adjoining* regions. If this were not so there would be no question of these various regions, and they would have to be united into one larger region. But two regions separated by other regions may sometimes show little difference with respect to this simple first integration. It depends on the real chorological differentiation of this integration in this part of the world or area.

Next every region is further divided on the ground of the chorological differentiation of some characteristics of a few other things of the complex which again show some interrelation with other, though less important, characteristics of the chorological differentiations of economic life. Here, too, it is possible that within the division of one region there are a few smaller regions that do not border on each other and show little or no difference with respect to this second integration.

We do not immediately divide this part of the world according to a complicated economic-geographic integration. For the ascertainment and the distinction of smaller regions it is first necessary to gain an insight into the nature of the chorological differentiation with respect to the economic-geographic integration of the whole area.

It is obviously impossible as a rule to determine *large* regions forming unities of a complicated integration. For the more complicated an integration is the greater the chorological differentiation at equal distances, and the simpler an integration is the smaller the chorological differentiation at the same distance. This is to say that with an increase in the complication of an integration there will be a decrease in the size of the region — which region forms a homogeneous uniform differentiation of that integration — and as its complication decreases the size of the region will increase. As we have already explained before, this is due to the semi-independence of the differentiation of things [68]. This is why we have made the first division according to a simple integration resulting in larger regions, and next we have subdivided these regions into smaller regions on the ground of a more complicated integration. These smaller regions also possess the characteristics of the larger region of which they are parts, and, consequently, they also have the characteristics of the first simple chorologically differentiated integration of the area that has been divided.

We have based this division on the chorological differentiation of the vertical interrelations and have determined vertical unities of region. It is necessary to supplement them with a division according to the chorological differentiation of the horizontal interconnections and horizontal unities of region (unities of relative location). The latter division must supplement and, if necessary, correct the former. (Chapter V).

How are we to describe a region as a vertical and as a horizontal unity in its difference from adjoining regions, and in its horizontal chorological interconnection with the other regions? This can be done with the aid of purely idiographic concepts and with the collective special concept [69].

The *elementary idiographic*, or the *elementary special concept*, is a combination of generic basic concepts. If we want to render a particular uniform chorological differentiation of an integration, i.e., a particular speciality of a small region, we do so with the aid of elementary idiographic concepts. If we want to describe a larger region, and this region consists of a number of smaller regions, some of which are nearly similar and others are different, we can do so by uniting the elementary special concepts of these smaller regions into a *higher idiographic concept*. This higher concept is a whole of characteristics, and in a certain sense it constitutes the least common multiple of the elementary concepts of the regional parts [70]. This higher concept, therefore, not only has a larger extension (a larger region) but also a greater connotation (more characteristics) than the elementary concepts from which it has been formed [71]. The characteristics of these idiographic concepts chiefly bear on the vertical interrelations. The small regions we discussed are vertical unities (uniform chorological extension of vertical interrelations). The large region is no vertical unity according to the characteristics of the higher idiographic concept. For there is no question in this case of a uniform extension of the vertical interrelations, because the vertical unities of the component minor regions are partly different. A higher idiographic concept is the sum total, and the least common multiple of the elementary idiographic concepts.

But the higher idiographic concept is more than the sum total of the elementary concepts: it is a whole of characteristics. The larger region forms a relative whole. It is the horizontal interconnections between the minor regions within the larger region which make the latter into a certain whole, and this whole also forms the parts of the larger region. The larger region is a horizontal unity. It is a *relative* whole, because there are also all kinds of interconnections between these minor regions with other regions outside of the larger region.

It is clear that the characteristics of the higher idiographic concept are only applicable to the larger region as a whole, and not to each of the regional parts separately. The characteristics of the elementary idiographic concept, however, apply to all the parts of the minor region concerned.

If the connotation of the higher idiographic concept becomes too comprehensive, and owing to the great number of characteristics this idiographic concept becomes unmanageable, we mostly proceed to a collective special concept. A *collective special concept* (Gruppenbegriff) looks for the common elements of the characteristics of special concepts of which it has been composed. In a certain sense it forms the greatest common divisor. The construction of a collective special concept is, consequently, generalizing, nomothetic. But the characteristics, though in a limited number, form a speciality. It is true, it is a generalization, but the connotation of the collective special concept only applies to that single matter, to that special region. In reality it is an idiographic concept. The collective special concepts, however, are often again the material for nomothetic, generic concepts and classifications and often form the starting point of the latter, but originally they are special concepts [72].

Collective special concepts and elementary special concepts often pass into one another. A region which we call a vertical unity according to certain standards, and is based on the idea of the uniform chorological extension of particular characteristics, is so only approximately. In fact it is a generalization, for only an earth point is uniform. By ignoring many slight deviations we can call a minor region uniform and homogeneous, and then such a region answers the requirements of an elementary idiographic concept. In reality, however, it is often a collective special concept. The characteristics of this concept are really formed by the common and predominant characteristics of the small parts of such a minor region. What is common and uniform is often the result of the fact that the collective special concept often expresses many characteristics within limits and in averages.

Collective special concepts are very important for rendering the chorological differentiation and the horizontal interconnection of the world or of a part of the earth.

186

In this connection let us think of two adjoining states that are mutually connected by close economic relations. Both consist of a number of economic-geographic regions, each of the latter forming a vertical and horizontal unity in our thought. Each region again has external horizontal interconnections with other regions within the state to which it belongs, and with regions of the other state. Let us distinguish these external horizontal interconnections, in the order of succession mentioned, into *a* and *b*. Those of *a* form the internal horizontal interconnections of each state apart, giving it a certain degree of horizontal unity. The external horizontal interconnections of *b* do not go straightway from a region of the one state to a region of the other state. These interconnections are mediated by the two states as separate wholes, as separate unities. Regulations concerning the import and the export, and other economic regulations are in force for all economic geographic regions of the two states apart. On this point the territory of the state is a unity. To distinguish the two states as chorological differentiants, and to determine their horizontal interconnection we conceive of the two countries as vertical unities. The characteristics of these vertical unities are determined by the collective special concepts of both states. The collective special concept is an extremely suitable concept in special geography to render the chorological differentiation in vertical unities of region.

Geography is concerned with the chorological differentiation of the totality of earthly things and phenomena. Owing to this differentiation, this difference of things and their phenomena, it is possible to speak of regions.

General geography looks for what is general within the chorological differentiation, and starts from a supposed law-conformity within the chorological differentiation. It tries to reduce the interminable differentiations to general differentiations by means of comparison. General geography has to deal with many regions of the earth surface, which it tries to consider as members of classes.

Special geography specifies and concentrates on the individual speciality of the chorological differentiation of particular areas, or definite parts of the world.

Essentially, general and special geography are both concerned with the chorological differentiation of the whole surface of the earth, because the latter is a continuum, and every region is a part of this manifold continuum.

General and special geography try to find unities of the total chorological differentiation resulting in unities of region. This unity is very restricted, but the possibilities to determine unities of a certain totality from a particular viewpoint are greater in special geography than in general geography.

There is a problem in science, especially in cultural science, about the question as to which is more important: the general characteristic that things have in common, or the special trait by which they are distinct from each other. At first sight it seems as if this problem does not concern geography. For geography has to do with chorological differentiation, consequently only with what is special, with the difference between earthly things and phenomena from one locality to another. As the general, and that which is common, apparently do not belong to the domain of geography, geography should not pronounce a judgment on the question as to whether or not the general is more important than the special. But things are not so simple as this. General geography looks for what is more general and what is less general of this differentiation, of this difference. Special geography generalizes with the aid of the collective special concept by paying attention to what is common in the characteristics of a region in its distinction from other regions.

So geography is certainly concerned with the problem about the importance of the general and the special, the more so as geography is anthropocentric and is related to many cultural phenomena [73].

With regard to geography we can, therefore, say, that the problem is reduced to the question: which is more important, the more general or the special of the characteristics of the regions by which these regions can be *distinguished* from each other.

In the last chapter of our work we have, therefore, been obliged to choose our position with respect to this problem. In the *distinction* of classes in general geography we have started from the idea that the more general characteristics are more fundamental than

188

the less general characteristics; and in our use of the collective special concept in special geography we have implicitly assumed that the common characteristics of a region in their *distinction* from those of other regions are very important. But at the end of this study we must declare that this difficult problem implies a great deal more than we have placed in the forefront.

CHAPTER VIII

SUMMARY

The investigation of the significance of the principle of chorological differentiation starts from the age-old definition of geography as the science of the earth surface (the world) in its spatial diversity. We prefer the concept world as the issue is not only concerned with physical and material things, but also with immaterial things on the earth surface. The term "chorological" should be preferred to the designation "spatial", because in the concept "space" the three dimensions are of equal value, whereas geography emphasizes the two dimensions that determine the surface. The third dimension is, as it were, a further determination of the other two dimensions. The old geographic concept "chora" implies this emphasis on two dimensions, just like the concepts "area and region" do.

Although it is generally accepted that all the geographic sciences have to do with the chorological differentiation of earthly things and phenomena, no emphasis is as a rule laid on it. On the contrary, the stress is much rather laid on the difference between physical and socio-cultural phenomena, and geography becomes something of secondary importance. That both are geography and that this characteristic is the first thing in physical as well as in social geography, is pushed into the background. This geographic element is the "gēa", but not the gēa in general, but in its chorological differentiation. Various geographers of this and the previous century have brought this element to the fore again. Ritter and later on Hettner have laid the foundation of this principle by distinguishing geography from history according to the principles of chorological differentation and the differentiation in time. Hartshorne has developed this idea further. Yet it cannot be said that the investigation of this matter has been finished. On the contrary; this holds especially for the relation between the chorological differentiation and the chorological horizontal interconnection. Our inquiry is chiefly focused on this. We are of the opinion that the significance and the deeper meaning of geography can be determined from the

relation between these two principles, in which the chorologica[
differentiation is the primary element.

What problems are raised, if we consider the idea of chorological
differentiation as the essential feature of geography?

Geography is concerned with the multifarious diversity of the
continuum of the world (the earth-surface), enclosing a totality of
earthly things and phenomena in every locality: the ground,
the soil, the water, the atmosphere, vegetation, the fauna, and the
material and immaterial things of man. This diversity, or this
chorological differentiation, is manifest in the existence of various
earth spaces, chorai, areas and regions. The question is: is an earth
space given, and does an earth space with all kinds of material
and immaterial things in it really exist, or is an earth space an "ens
rationis", and do the dimensions of things determine an earth
space? We are adherents of the latter opinion. An earth space or
chora (country, area, region) is constituted by the earthly things and
their dimensions, of which the two dimensions determining the
surface are geographically the most important.

In every earth point things and their phenomena are more or
less integrated, but these things and phenomena are not differentiated in perfectly the same way; there is semi-independent chorological differentiation. A clay region and an adjoining low peat
soil form two chorological differentiants of the soil, but both
regions often have the same grass vegetation and the same form of
production, viz., pastoral farming and dairy farming: there is
only one vegetation region, and only one economic region. Regions
as unities can only be determined according to one thing in connection with a few other things. Thus there are various unities
of geographic totality to be distinguished. In every totality one
thing with its phenomena are the nucleus to which some other
things with their phenomena are related which have a great influence on this nucleus, and which form a unity in their mutual
integration. This integration we call a vertical interrelation. This
interrelation is found at every earth point, and the maximal uniform chorological extension of this vertical interrelation we call a
vertical unity. There is also another integration: dissimilar things
are not only interrelated in the same locality, but many

things of one locality are also integrated with things of other localities, both with neighbouring localities and with things at a greater distance. This integration we call horizontal interconnection. This interconnection is a process of movement based on mutual relative location. Adjacent localities possessing a stronger interconnection with each other than with adjoining localities, form an internal horizontal unity. The horizontal interconnections with localities and regions outside of them, either adjoining or at a greater distance, or even at a very great distance, we call external horizontal interconnections.

The chorological differentiation of the world then appears from a chorological differentiation of geographic regions forming vertical unities, and from a chorological differentiation of internal horizontal unities of region, which latter is, consequently, a differentiation of unities of relative location. And finally, there is one more kind of differentiation, viz., that of the external horizontal interconnections over the earth surface.

The vertical unities of region are most marked as chorological differentiants. As we have already observed, regions are formed by the two dimensions of the surface of things forming these particular chorological differentiations, the ground being the fixed datum for the determination of the extension of the chorological differentiation. Just like the atmosphere the ground of a region has an absolute uninterrupted extension. The ground is the prerequisite of all other earthly things. These other things are found and rest on and in the ground, and human beings are found and move about on the ground. The ground is conceivable without the other earthly things, but the latter are not conceivable without the ground. Of course this does not mean that the ground would be what it is, if the other things on and in it were not there; nor does it mean that the chorological differentiation of the ground always determines the chorological differentiation of all the other things. The ground has an absolute extension, the other things of a region are found on the ground in a more or less dense spread. Size and form of a geographic region are, consequently, determined by the chorological extension of the piece of ground on which we find the things that are interrelated and display a chorological differentiation.

A geographic region is determined by the extension of the chorological differentiation of this integration on the ground, independent
of the question whether or not the piece of ground there forms a
chorological differentiation, if at least the ground itself is not the
nucleus of the integration.

A thing is geographic if it differentiates over the earth surface;
it is all the more geographically significant as its chorological differentiation influences the differentiation of other earthly things,
or is influenced by the chorological differentiation of other earthly
things, i.e., if there is question of a totality of chorological differentiation. But there is another point from which the significance of
chorological differentiation is determined. A chorological differen-
titation is geographically important, if it is significant to man, man
being considered as the principle inhabitant of the earth surface.
Geography is anthropocentric. The evaluation of the chorological
differentiation of the earth is determined in geography from the
point of view that the regions are the living spaces of human groups.
This also holds where no human beings live, and which only consist
of physical and organic things. Then, too, the significance of the
chorological differentiation of these things is determined by the
significance they have to the human inhabitants of adjoining regions
and those lying further away.

As has been said before, we distinguish a chorological differentiation of vertical unities of region from that of the horizontal
unities of region. A region is never a unity (a homogeneous and
uniform chorological differentiant) of the whole complex of things.
As a unity a region is formed by some characteristics of a few
things of the complex, and determined according to the standards
we apply to the chorological differentiation. If we concentrate
on some characteristics of other things of the complex, we shall
obtain another region of a different chorological extension. Even
the smallest topographical basic units (geotopes and ecotopes) are
no units of the whole complex, but have been formed according to
particular characteristics of the soil and depend on our standards.

Unities of region are determinable in reality, but they also
contain many other things that do not form a unity within these
regions.

193

The unities of region we form do not lie apart and isolated from each other, but are connected with each other by external horizontal interconnections. Owing to these horizontal interconnections there is *unity in diversity*. From this view-point the significance of chorological differentiation becomes clear. It must be determined by means of the comparison with the differentiation in time.

Parallel to a geographic chorological differentiation and the chorological horizontal interconnection of the chorological differentiants (geographic regions) are the historical differentiation in time and the historical interconnection of the different periods. Every geographic concept proceeding from the principle of chorological differentiation must have its counter-pole, a historical concept proceeding from the differentiation in time. The gist of this argument is found in the opposition of region to period. A region is a chorological unity in a definite time. The earth surface forms a mosaic of regions at a particular time. A period is a unity of time and bound to a particular piece of the earth surface. History forms a chain of periods on a particular piece of the earth surface. There is, however, not only a difference in aspect, there is also partly a difference in the kind of things that are the objects of geography and history. The object of geography is the chorological totality in which the ground and the nature of the earth surface are very important. The things investigated by history are above all of a social, political, and cultural nature; history happens to a people or a group of peoples. But the difference between the objects is also determined by the difference between the aspects. For the ground and nature are differentiated over the earth surface to a much higher degree in a particular length of time than the ground and nature of a definite piece of the earth surface differentiate in course of time. Geography, which studies the chorological differentiation of the world at a particular time, and mostly at the time in which we live, is above all focused on the ground and on nature, and on those cultural phenomena that are integrated with nature. This integration does not possess a deterministic, but a conditional character, and usually a certain mutuality. History first of all concentrates on political, cultural and social phenomena, which change in course of time. Between geography and history there are many transitional forms, such as geology and historical geography. The two aspects can be distinguished indeed, but they cannot be separated: The history of a human group happens on a particular piece of the earth surface, but in every period it is influenced by the history of other human groups on other pieces of the earth surface owing to horizontal interconnections in every period, and the geographic mosaic of regions of the world at the present time is not apart from the mosaics of regions of the past.

If we want to understand the meaning and the significance of geography we must emphasize its aspect, i.e., the chorological differentiation of the world at the time in which we live. As an investigator does not examine the chorological differentiation of the world as a whole, except in global studies, his attention is mostly directed to one country, one area, one region. Then the problem must be posited like this: What is this region like, and what are its interconnections with other, especially with adjoining regions? In both chorological differentiation is the essential thing. What a region is like is determined by its difference from other regions. For on the ground of the difference from other regions, especially from adjoining regions, we speak of *this* region. Its indication rests on it. Especially owing to this difference from other regions there is horizontal interconnection with other regions. The differences give rise to the horizontal processes of movement. The various regions cannot do without each other. Chorological differentiation appears to have a horizontal chorological directedness. In a certain sense this chorological finality is at the same time the norm of geography. A region answers its purpose if its own peculiarity (its difference from other regions) has been developed and directed to the speciality of other regions. It provides for other regions, and in return receives something of what is peculiar to these regions. Such a region participates in the chorological differentiation, in the rich diversity of a larger part of the world. This region fills and replenishes the earth. A region misses its purpose, if it is needlessly isolated and has its peculiarity, its difference from other regions, turned into an antithesis, into a contrast. Then the unity in diversity gets lost. In our view the meaning of geography is to be found in the principle of the chorological differentiation of the earth surface at the time in which we live, which chorological differentiation forms a unity owing to the horizontal interconnection. For every region (chorological differentiant) the geographical problem is: How does the region function in its peculiarity within a whole of regions?

The result of the chorological differentiation of the world is revealed in chorological differentiants, in regions. They are determined by their difference in characteristics, but not all the characteristics differ. There are also similar characteristics. On the ground of these common characteristics there is partly question of regions of a certain type. The problem arises whether we can speak of classes of regions. General geography tries to ascertain by means of analysis and comparison in how far particular characteristics of regions recur, and whether there is any regularity within the chorological differentiation. If it is possible to subsume the characteristics under generic concepts, under classes, the regions possessing these characteristics are in a certain sense members of these classes.

The conception of a region as a member of a class is subject to severe restriction. A region really contains the extension of a complex of things of a greater or less degree of chorological differentiation. A geographic region is only a unity according to the differentiation of one thing in interrelation with the characteristics of the chorological differentiations of some other things of the complex. This thing and these interrelated things, however, are *interwoven* with the other things of the complex. In a certain sense, therefore, it is possible to consider the whole complex of a region according to these charateristics of the chorological differentiation of this one thing in interrelation with some other things. Only on the basis of this restricted unity is a region a member of a class.

Division and classification are to us no purpose as such, but a means to determine the order, the hierarchy of the characteristics of the regions. The various regions that are members of different classes can be investigated further as to their similarity and their dissimilarity. The similarity is the result of their belonging to one and the same super-class, the dissimilarity is due to their belonging to different subordinate classes. As the issue is concerned with their differentiation, with their difference, this similarity is ultimately considered in its difference from the similarity of other regions belonging to another super-class. In this way it is possible to establish the order of the importance of the characteristics of the regions. In how far general geography can form classes is, therefore, dependent on the question as to whether it is possible to apply the rules of a logical division. This possibility is chiefly governed by the question as to whether there is a hierarchy to be found in the characteristics of things that recur over the whole of the earth surface. We think there is indeed.

Geographic classes are no genetic classes, and regions as members of a class are no individuals like the members of a biological class. In size and form regions are often different in dependence on the characteristics by reason of which a class has been determined. It is not the genetically important characteristics, but those characteristics of a chorologically differentiating thing that are significant, which are interrelated with the characteristics of other things of the earthly complex that differentiate chorologically at the time in which we live. Classes and generic (nomothetic) concepts chiefly bear on vertical interrelations and vertical unities of region, and to a less degree on the horizontal interconnections and horizontal unities of region.

Special or regional geography investigates a region with the aid of the generic concepts and classes, especially with the aid of basic concepts ascertained by general geography. There are two ways of forming special or idiographic concepts: 1. The combination of generic characteristics is unique (einmalig), it is true, but it remains restricted, and is made in such a manner that all these characteristics hold for all the parts of this region; this is a collective special concept. It applies to a region as a vertical unity. 2. The combination of general characteristics is complete and the special concept is applicable to the region as a whole, but it is not applicable to its parts separately; this is the genuine idiographic concept. It constitutes the sum and the whole of the characteristics of the vertical interrelations of the regional parts, but not all the characteristics apply to the whole region as a vertical unity. The unity of the whole of the characteristics is especially determined by the internal horizontal interconnections and by the unity of the external horizontal interconnections.

197

General and special geography both concentrate on the totality of the chorological differentiation, and look for regions which in this respect possess a certain degree of unity. This unity, however, is restricted, and this restriction is even stronger in general geography than in special geography.

So general and special geography have both to do with the chorological differentiation, with the *difference* between earthly things from one locality to another, and with the interconnection of things of the various localities. Chorological differentiation results in a diversity of interconnected regions. General geography looks for what is general, just as special geography looks for what is special in the difference and in the interconnection of regions.

NOTES

CHAPTER I

INTRODUCTION

1   Hettner (a), p. 117.
2   Hettner (a), p. 116.
3   Hettner (a), p. 129
4   Hettner (a), pp. 116 and 129.
5   Hettner (a), pp. 114, 115.
6   Hettner (a), pp. 114—117.
Cf. also Hartshorne (a), pp. 130—148, 237—247.
Ditto (b), pp. 173—182.
7   De Jong (a).
8   Ritter, p. 152.
9   Van Paassen, p. 340.
10   Von Richthofen, p. 25.
Hettner (a), p. 122.
11   Hettner (b), I, p. 3.
12   Hartshorne (b), p. 17.
13   Keuning (a), p. 23.
14   Cools (b), pp. 9—15.
Van der Valk, pp. 82—92, 93—107.
Verstege, pp. 3—17.
De Vooys, p. 14 ff.
Cools, (a).
Keuning (c), pp. 11—18.
Kuperus, pp. 489, 490. His criticism of the French and the Utrecht Schools has been published in a very shortened form on the pages mentioned.
15   Vidal de la Blache (a), p. 299.
16   Vidal de la Blache (b), pp. 3, 6, 7.
17   Cools (b), p. 17.

CHAPTER II

CHOROLOGICAL DIFFERENTIATION AND REGION

1   Van Dale, s.v. Wereld, sub 3.
2   Hettner (a), pp. 125—129, 231.
3   Carol (a), e.g. pp. 113—114.
Carol (b), a.o. pp. 92, 94.
4   Bobek und Schmithüsen, pp. 112—116.
Of the comprehensive mass of literature on the concept landscape we would make special mention of:
Bürger, especially pp. 29—75.
Passarge, pp. 331—337.

Kuperus, pp. 490—500.
Krebs (b), Tome II. Rapports pp. 207—213.
Troll, pp. 164, 165, 166—171.
Hartshorne (a), pp. 149—174, 250—284.
Paffen.
On the difference between the terms landscape and region:
Carol (b), p. 94.
Schmitthenner (c), p. 14.

[5] Ritter, p. 152. "The geographical sciences are especially concerned with the spaces of the earth surface in so far as they are terrestrially filled (no matter the natural kingdom they belong to or the forms they may assume)..." Ritter and his contemporaries conceived of nature as objective reality, all that exists outside of the investigator's mind.
Hartshorne (a), p. 298.

[6] Filosofisch Lexicon, s.v. Ruimte, the third conception.

[7] In this connection we refer to:
Hartshorne (b), pp. 129—143, especially p. 142.
Wooldridge and East, pp. 140—160.
Edwards.
Ackerman, p. 15.
Gilbert, pp. 345—347, ff.
James, pp. 8—15.
Whittlesey (b), pp. 19—68, especially pp. 21, 22, 32—51.
Troll, pp. 164—165.
Bürger, pp. 29—75.
Le Lannou, pp. 163—166.
Sorre, Vol. III, L'Habitat, pp. 445—450.

[8] Hartshorne (a), Chapter IX.
Schmitthenner (c), pp. 16—19.

[9] Nature and culture are vague notions. If we take the former concept to mean the part of reality that is independent of man, in contradistinction to the part that is man's, we must remember that also in our study many things are indicated by the word nature which in reality are not purely natural, but partly belong to both man and his culture. The soil we usually call a thing of nature, also in the present investigation, has been cultivated by man in very many areas for centuries at a stretch. It is therefore partly natural and partly cultural, a capital good. The same thing holds for vegetation. Natural vegetation is found only where man has not yet influenced and modified it. The vegetation of most areas has been modified by human culture and is something that is influenced both by natural and cultural factors. Other things that we call culture and consider to be things of man are really also the products of nature. Material cultural possessions, capital goods, have been made from material things of nature. The things of nature and those of man are very often so closely interwoven that it is impossible to subsume them under one single category. When in this study the terms nature and culture are repeatedly used, it should be remembered that they render their conceptual content only approximately.
Cf. also Hartshorne (a), pp. 296 ff.
Hartshorne (b), pp. 48—54.
Demangeon, pp. 28, 29. Demangeon speaks of the geographical environment,

i.e., the physical environment modified by man and the social environment.
Dijkmans, p. 11, ff.
Le Lannou, pp. 91—95.

10   Hettner (a), p. 222. "Geographical significance attaches to all the facts of the earth surface that are different in different terrestrial localities, and whose differences are causally related with the differences of other facts, which are therefore characteristic of these countries, landscapes, and localities". Cf. also p. 129.

Hartshorne (a), p. 463: "Geography seeks to acquire a complete knowledge of the areal differentiation of the world, and therefore discriminates among the phenomena that vary in different parts of the world only in terms of their geographical significance — i.e., their relation to the total differentiation of areas".

11   Polspoel, p. 41.
12   Cf. also: Bobek und Schmithüsen, pp. 112, 113.
Carol (a), pp. 115, 116; (b), pp. 94, 95.

CHAPTER III

ANALYSIS OF THE VERTICAL CHOROLOGICAL COMPLEX

1   De Jong (a), pp. 13—29, 81—88.
Hartshorne (a), pp. 250—284.
Schmitthenner (c), pp. 7—37. In this important publication the problem about a landscape is in the centre. S. combats the conception of a landscape as an individual and as an organism.
Hettner (a), pp. 129, 275—281, 285—287, 291—317.
2   Hettner (a), p. 308.
3   Hartshorne (a), pp. 250—311.
4   De Jong (a), pp. 13—21.
5   Bobek und Schmithüsen, pp. 112, 113.
6   Von Handel, pp. 659—664, especially 660, 661.
Von Weizsäcker, p. 129.
7   Schmithüsen, pp. 74—83.
8   Troll, pp. 162—181.
9   Paffen, 1953.
10   Paffen, pp. 39—43.
11   De Jong (a), p. 48.
Hartshorne (a), p. 322.
Thornthwaite (a), pp. 633—655.
De Jong (c), pp. 20—30.
Huntington, 1924.
Huntington and Cushing, pp. 399—416.
12   De Jong (a), pp. 27—30, 41—43.
On the appreciation of nature by man and the function of nature in economic life, cf. Zimmermann, Part I: Introduction to the Study of Resources, pp. 3—143; especially pp. 85—90; first edition, 1933, pp. 85—91.
De Jong (a).
Keuning (c), pp. 11—18.

Den Hollander, espec. pp. 240—271, 389—392.
Le Lannou, pp. 60—90.
Sorre, Vol. II (1, 2). Les fondements techniques.
13 Edelman (b), pp. 8—12.
Ditto (a), pp. 106—118.
Bengtson and Van Royen, p. 110.
Finch and Trewartha, pp. 443—453.
14 Langeveld, pp. 55—60. A concept is a unity, and it is not determined
by an arbitrary junction of elements (characteristics of the matter concerned).
The unity is a totality which determines the parts.
15 Het Westen en Overig Nederland, p. 22.
16 Hartshorne (a), pp. 334, 335.
17 Hartshorne (a), p. 351.
18 Hartshorne (a), p. 300.
19 Hartshorne (b), p. 44.
20 Schmitthenner (c), p. 19. Plewe (b), pp. 411, 413, 414.
21 A. Cholley (a), p. 121. It may be worth while to consider Cholley's conception. In this connection he says: "Geography is essentially anthropocentric". In the second edition of his book, which has been entirely changed, his
pronouncement has been weakened, we think. He then refers to man's significance as "a geographical agent of the first order", and he speaks of "the
part man plays in geography". This is, of course a little different from saying
that the importance of terrestrial things is determined by the significance that
things have to man, because man is the principal inhabitant of the earth. But
then he repeats his well-known statement: "The conception that a geographer
forms of man differs remarkably from that of a philosopher or of a historian.
Geographical man is a part of the planetary biological domain, and as such
he can be considered as the principal inhabitant of the planet".
Cholley (b), p. 22.
Cholley's pronouncement should not be confounded with that of Le Lannou.
The latter says: "Human geography is the science of man as an inhabitant".
pp. 11, 16. This definition is of a much more neutral character and does not
call man the most important inhabitant.
22 Hartshorne (b), pp. 44—47.
23 Hartshorne (b), p. 46.
24 De Jong (a), on this and on what follows cf. pp. 30—37.
25 Von Humboldt, II, p. 89.
26 Hartshorne (a), pp. 308, 309, 390.
27 Hartshorne (a), pp. 275, 395.
28 Schmitthenner (c), pp. 15, 16, 19, 20, 27, 32.
Ditto (b), pp. 92, 95, 96.
29 Cf. also: De Jong (b).

CHAPTER IV

GEOTOPES AND VERTICAL CHOROLOGICAL UNITIES

1 Troll, p. 170.
2 Schmithüsen, pp. 74—83.

3   Paffen, pp. 80, 86.
4   Paffen, pp. 86, 87.
5   Paffen, pp. 87—90, 96—99.
Troll, pp. 170—174.
6   Paffen, p. 90.
7   Paffen, pp. 98, 99.
8   Paffen, pp. 106, 107.
9   Paffen, pp. 107 ff., 128 (list).
Unstead, pp. 175—187.
10   Paffen, pp. 75, 76, 80—82.
11   Paffen, pp. 158, 159.
12   Paffen, pp. 98, 99.
13   Paffen, pp. 98, 102, 106—108.
14   Paffen, p. 72.
15   Paffen, pp. 72, 90.
Troll, pp. 170—174.
16   Hartshorne (a), pp. 250—311, 395.
17   Schmitthenner (c), esp. pp. 15, 16, 19, 20, 27, 28, 32. Cf. also
Schmitthenner (b), pp. 92, 95, 96.
18   Carol (a), pp. 128—131.
19   De Jong (a), pp. 13—58.
20   Schmitthenner (c), p. 18.
21   Schmitthenner (c), p. 19. Plewe (b), p. 413.
22   Hartshorne (a), pp. 356, 452, 456.
23   Hartshorne (a), p. 419.
24   Hartshorne (a), p. 415.

CHAPTER V

UNITIES OF VERTICAL INTERRELATION AND HORIZONTAL
INTERCONNECTION AS THE BASIS OF CHOROLOGICAL
DIFFERENTIATION

1   Ullman, pp. 56, 60. Also Ackerman emphasizes spatial interaction.
Especially pp. 5, 8, 24—26, 32—34.
2   Hartshorne (b), p. 19.
3   De Jong (a), pp. 13—29, 82—93.
Cf. also Hartshorne (a), pp. 275, 281, 282, and further 262—276.
Hartshorne (b), pp. 134—145.
4   Hartshorne (b), p. 117, and also p. 137.
5   Cf. also Hartshorne (a), p. 395.
6   In another context. Cf. Hartshorne (b), pp. 135, 136.
7   Cf. also: De Jong (b), pp. 7, 8.
8   Hettner (a), pp. 129, 279, 291, 309.
Ditto (b), I, pp. 66—69.
9   Hettner (b), I. pp. 66—69.
Van Paassen, pp. 334 and ff.
Cf. also: Ritter, pp. 103, 104, 183.

10   Paffen, pp. 98, 99.
11   Cf. also Hartshorne (a), p. 395.
12   Hartshorne (a), pp. 395, 297. Cf. also: p. 275.
13   For an explanation of "ens rationis" in general cf.
Hoogveld (a), I, pp. 17—19.
Ditto (b), I, pp. 24—27.
14   Schmitthenner (c), pp. 16, cf. also 28, 29.
15   Hartshorne (b), p. 136 and pp. 129—145.
16   Carol (a), pp. 123—125.

CHOROLOGICAL DIFFERENTIATION AND INTERCONNECTION VERSUS HISTORICAL CHANGE AND DEVELOPMENT

1   Hettner (a), pp. 117, 116.
2   Hettner (a), p. 129.
3   Hettner (a), p. 122.
Hettner (b), I. p. 3.
4   Hettner (a), pp. 116, 129.
5   Ritter, p. 152.
6   Van Paassen, pp. 333—335.
7   Schmitthenner (b), p. 45.
8   Hettner (a), pp.114—117.
9   Van Paassen, p. 333 ff.
10   Hartshorne (a), p. 373.
11   Hartshorne (a), pp. 283, 284.
12   Hartshorne (a), p. 373.
13   Hartshorne (a), pp. 410, 411.
Hartshorne (b), p. 167.
14   Creutzburg, p. 413.
15   Hartshorne (a), p. 445, Cf. also pp. 178, 181, 182, 259.
16   De Jong (b), p. 14.
17   Hartshorne (a), pp. 184—188, 397.
18   Hartshorne (a), p. 185.
19   Hartshorne (a), pp. 410, 411.
20   Hartshorne (a), p. 185.
21   Kroeber, pp. 545, 546. In this connection compare also Hartshorne's
further, more exact, definition of geography and history. (a), pp. 183, 283, 284.
22   Hartshorne (a), p. 185.
23   Cf. also: De Jong (d), pp. 102, 112, 113.
Hartshorne (a), p. 373.
24   Hartshorne (b), p. 103, cf. also p. 107.
25   De Jong (a), p. 80. Hettner (b), I, pp. 39, 40, and Hartshorne (a), pp.
176—182. In this connection it is also important to study Le Lannou, pp. 41, 42.
26   Cf. also: Hartshorne (a), pp. 182—184.
De Jong (a), pp. 80, 81.
27   Bobek and Schmithüsen, especially pp. 112—115.

28 Jones, pp. 376, 377.
29 Clark, pp. 71—73.
30 Hözel, pp. 378—396, 433—444.
Cf. also: Hettner (a), pp. 299—317.
31 Plewe (a), pp. 28—46.
32 Schmitthenner (b).
33 Van Paassen.
34 Schmitthenner (b), p. 81.
35 Van Paassen, p. 335.
36 Van Paassen, p. 335 ff.
37 Van Paassen, pp. 334, 348.
38 Van Paassen, pp. 336—339.
39 Schmitthenner (b), especially pp. 57, 81—86, 93—96.
40 We are referring to the religion of the Hindus who spare the lives of two hundred million cows without putting them to much economic use; and also the lives of perhaps a far larger number of goats which not only feed on grass but also on the leaves of the trees, so that it is impossible for any new vegetation to grow on the hillside, and the soil is radically destroyed by erosion. De Vries, p. 54.
41 Cf. also: Schmitthenner (c), pp. 16, 19, 28/29.
42 Cf. also: De Jong (d), pp. 97—119. When that study was published, we were still unacquainted with the lecture that Norbert Krebs had delivered in 1923, entitled: "Natur- und Kulturlandschaft". In the latter part of 1959 we came across this lecture. In conclusion of his argument Krebs advances a thought that also plays a rôle in our own study mentioned above, as well as in the present study, although in a different context and on a different basis. Krebs says: "Thus to me it is only the elaboration of the recognised correct thought that the art of the geographer consists in his conceiving the countries (Länderräume) as a unity, not only as regards their content, but also with respect to that which their surroundings give them, as well as that which these countries have to offer their surroundings". Krebs (a), p. 94.
43 Cf. De Jong (a), pp. 94—97.
44 Other authors, too, such as Keuning, Le Lannou, and Sorre, although they do not emphasize the principle of chorological differentiation at the present time as we do, they point to the principle of the function of a locality and a region with respect to other localities and regions.
Keuning (b), pp. 12, 13.
Keuning (d), pp. 342 ff.
Le Lannou, pp. 177—189.
Sorre, III. pp. 24—27, 179, 231—246, 362—366.

CHAPTER VII

THE GENERAL AND THE SPECIAL WITHIN CHOROLOGICAL DIFFERENTIATION

1 Windelband, pp. 145 ff.
Rickert, (b), pp. 38—60.

205

2   Rickert, (a); Cf. also: (b), pp. 17—28, 38—60, 78—101.
3   Graf, cf. especially pp. 14—73. Cf. also: De Jong(a), pp. 60-73.
4   Eucken, p. 53.
5   Hettner (a), pp. 221—224.
6   Hartshorne (a), pp. 366—459.
7   De Jong (a), pp. 59—81.
Ditto (b), pp. 15—19.
8   Cf. also: De Jong (a).
9   Hartshorne (b).
10   Schmitthenner (a), pp. 123—137.
Ditto (c).
11   Bobek, pp. 122—145.
12   De Jong (c), pp. 20—30.
13   Hartshorne (b), pp. 108—145. Especially: pp. 116, 118—122, 126, 129,
142—145. Cf. also pp. 163, 182.
14   Hartshorne (b), pp. 119, 121, 122, 129, 144.
15   Hartshorne (b), pp. 119 and 144.
16   Hartshorne (b), pp. 116 and 119.
17   Schmitthenner (c), pp. 14, 15; cf. also p. 13. Ditto (a), p. 125.
18   Schmitthenner (c), p. 36.
Cf. also: Kuperus, pp. 500—502.
19   Van den Berg, pp. 134—143.
Filosofisch Lexicon, pp. 285, 322, 329.
Bakker, pp. 322—324.
Stebbing (a), pp. 74—80, 99—114.
20   Hartshorne (a), pp. 378—397. Especially pp. 384—391.
De Jong (a), pp. 65—75.
21   Hartshorne (a), pp. 182—184. Cf. also pp. 389—391.
22   Schmitthenner (c), p. 33.
23   Cf. also: Stebbing (b), p. 436.
24   Hartshorne (a), p. 373.
25   Hartshorne (a), p. 388.
26   Hettner (a), p. 309.
27   Van den Berg, pp. 116—122, 226, 227 (notes 78 and 79) and pp. 8—10.
Stebbing (b), p. 434.
Cf. also: Hartshorne (a), p. 387.
28   Stebbing (a), pp. 107—109.
Stebbing (b), pp. 434, 435.
29   Van den Berg, pp. 120, 121.
30   Stebbing (b), p. 438.
Van den Berg, pp. 134—144.
31   Van den Berg, pp. 139, 143.
Stebbing (a), pp. 104, 105.
32   Stebbing (a), p. 108.
33   Stebbing (b), p. 436.
34   Schmitthenner (c), pp. 14—17, 27.
35   Stebbing (b), p. 439.
36   Stebbing (b), p. 439.

[37] Thornthwaite (a), pp. 633—655. This has been used in: (b), pp. 433—440. Thornthwaite (c), pp. 55—94.

[38] Thornthwaite (c), p. 88.

Cf. also: De Jong (a), pp. 48—51.

[39] Thornthwaite (a), pp. 644, 645 and (b), p. 433.

[40] Thornthwaite (a), pp. 647, 648.

[41] Hartshorne (a), p. 323. "For example, in Koeppen's system, there is no more reason for relating the types Cfa and Csa as subdivisions of C, than there would be to relate Cfa and Dfa (in the form Fca and Fda) as sub-divisions of a major group F (ample rain all year)".

[42] Thornthwaite (a), pp. 649, 654, 655.

[43] Bengtson and Van Royen, p. 95.

[44] Thornthwaite (b), map of the world: Climates of the Earth.

[45] Hettner (a), p. 400. Cf. also: pp. 278, 280.

Hettner (b), I. pp. 3, 69; IV. p. 308.

[46] Hartshorne (a), pp. 350—356; Cf. also: pp. 334—346.

[47] Whittlesey (a), pp. 199—240. Cf. also Hartshorne (a), pp. 340—352.

[48] Hartshorne and Dicken (b),

Hartshorne and Dicken (a), pp. 99—120.

Dicken, especially pp. 16—31.

[49] Bengtson and Van Royen.

[50] Boesch.

[51] Erde und Weltwirtschaft, herausgegeben von R. Lütgens. Bd. I-V. In this context Bd. II and III are of special importance.

[52] Cf. also: De Jong (a), pp. 76—79.

[53] Wooldridge and East, p. 146.

[54] De Jong (a), pp. 59, 60.

[55] Bobek, p. 122.

[56] Bobek, pp. 137—139 ff.

[57] Cf. also: Bobek und Schmithüsen, p. 114.

Cf. also: Winkler; in this connection: De Jong (b), pp. 13, 15 ff.

[58] Hartshorne (a), p. 390.

[59] Hartshorne (a), p. 391.

[60] Hartshorne (a), p. 389.

[61] Hettner (a), pp. 223 (at the top), 308 (in the middle).

[62] Hettner (a), p. 314: "Moreover, the importance of the differences or relations by no means always corresponds with the position in the system of causes: many genetically subordinate contrasts are among the greatest in existence as regards their influence, and should, therefore, be given a prominent place in a geographic division".

Cf. also p. 309: "The greatest difference on the earth surface is that between land and sea. It is true, genetically it is later, ... But with respect to the earth surface as the latter presents itself to our view ... this difference is more important than any other difference ...".

[63] Schaefer, pp. 226—249.

[64] Hartshorne (a), especially pp. 378—397, 413—436. Further pp. 292—365.

[65] Bobek, p. 124.

[66] Hartshorne (a), p. 243. Cf. also: p. 284 (in the middle).

[67] Krebs (c), cf. pp. 4—8, 115—136, 183, 184.

68   Cf. also: Hartshorne (b), pp. 119—121, 144.

69   Rickert (b), pp. 106 ff.; Graf, pp. 20 ff. and De Jong (a), pp. 62, 81—88.

70   De Jong (a), p. 62. Cf. also: Graf, pp. 103, 104.

71   Graf, p. 28.

72   In our opinion it is not correct to include collective special concepts in general geography, as Graf does. pp. 59, 60, 117, 118. Partly deviating from that which we wrote a few years ago (De Jong (a), p. 88), we are of opinion that this concept belongs to special geography. Cf. also: Hartshorne (a), p. 446.

73   Cf. also: De Jong (a), pp. 72, 73.

REFERENCES

ACKERMAN, E. A. Geography as a Fundamental Research Discipline. Chicago, 1958.

AMERICAN GEOGRAPHY. Inventory and Prospect. Ed. by P. E. James and C. F. Jones. Syracuse, 1954.

BAKKER, B.R. Over het gebruik van het ideaaltype in enkele natuurwetenschappen. Mens en Maatschappij, 32 (1957), pp. 321—334.

BENGTSON, N. A. and VAN ROYEN, W. Fundamentals of economic geography. 4th ed. Englewood Cliffs, N. J., 1956.

BERG, I. J. M. VAN DEN. Logica I. Inleiding — Begripsleer. 3rd print. Nijmegen — Utrecht, 1947.

BOBEK, H. Gedanken über das logische System der Geographie. Mitteilungen der Geographischen Gesellschaft in Wien, XCIX (1957). pp. 122—145.

BOBEK, H. and SCHMITHÜSEN, J. Die Landschaft im logischen System der Geographie. Erdkunde, III (1949), pp. 112—120.

BOESCH, H. H. Die Wirtschaftslandschaften der Erde. Zürich, 1947.

BÜRGER, K. Der Landschaftsbegriff. Dresdner Geographische Studien. Heft 7. Dresden, 1935.

CAROL, H. (a). Zur Diskussion um Landschaft und Geographie. Geographica Helvetica, XI (1956), pp. 111—133.

CAROL, H. (b). Grundsätzliches zum Landschaftsbegriff. Petermanns Geographischen Mitteilungen, CI (1957), pp. 93—98.

CHOLLEY, A. (a). Guide de l'Étudiant en Géographie. Paris, 1942.

CHOLLEY, A. (b). La Géographie (Guide de l'Étudiant) 2e éd. Paris, 1951.

CLARK, A. H. Historical Geography. In: American Geography. Inventory and Prospect. Syracuse, 1954, pp. 70—105.

COOLS, R. H. A. (a). De geografische gedachte bij Jean Brunhes. Diss. Utrecht, 1942.

COOLS, R. H. A. (b), Wisselend kennisobject der sociale geografie. (Inaugural lecture, University of Nijmegen). Groningen, 1959.

CREUTZBURG, N. Über den Werdegang von Kulturlandschaften. Zeitschrift der Gesellschaft für Erdkunde zu Berlin. Sonderband 1928, pp. 412—425.

DALE, VAN. van Dale's Nieuw Groot Woordenboek der Nederlandse Taal. 7th printing. The Hague, 1950. — World, see under „Wereld 3.".

DE JONG, G. See under Jong, G. de.

DEMANGEON, A. Problèmes de Géographie humaine. 3e éd. Paris, 1947.

DE VOOYS, A. C. See under Vooys, A. C. de.

DEN HOLLANDER, A. N. J. See under Hollander, A. N. J. den.

DICKEN, S. N. A Regional Economic Geography. Boston, 1949.

DYKMANS, G. Introduction critique à la science économique. Vol. II, 1. Le milieu géographique. Brussels, 1945.

EDELMAN, C. H. (a). Sociale en economische bodemkunde. Amsterdam, 1949.

EDELMAN, C. H. (b). Inleiding tot de bodemkunde van Nederland. Amsterdam, 1950.

EDWARDS, K. C. Land, Area and Region. (Inaugural lecture, University of Nottingham, 1950)

E.N.S.I.E. Vol. V. De Aarde. Amsterdam, 1948.

ERDE UND WELTWIRTSCHAFT. Herausgegeben von R. Lütgens. Bd. I—V.

209

Stuttgart, 1950—1957, especially *Bd. II*—Lütgens, R. Die Produktionsräume der Weltwirtschaft. 1952. *Bd. III*—Otremba, E. Allgemeine Agrar- und Industriegeographie. 1953.

EUCKEN, W. Die Grundlagen der Nationalökonomie. 5th printing. Godesberg, 1947.

FILOSOFISCH LEXICON. Compiled by J. Grooten and G. Jo Steenbergen. Antwerp — Amsterdam, 1958.

FINCH, V. C. and TREWARTHA, G. T. Elements of Geography. Physical and Cultural. 3rd ed. New York — Toronto — London, 1949.

GEOGRAPHY, American. See American Geography.

GEOGRAPHY IN THE TWENTIETH CENTURY. Ed. by G. Taylor. New York—London, 1951.

GILBERT, E. W. Geography and Regionalism. In: Geography in the Twentieth Century, New York—London, 1951. pp. 345—371.

GRAF, O. Vom Begriff der Geographie im Verhältnis zu Geschichte und Naturwissenschaft. München—Berlin, 1925.

HANDEL, P. VON. Kausalität, Finalität, Determination und Freiheit. Studium Generale, III. Berlin etc. 1950, pp. 659—664.

HARTSHORNE, R. (a). The Nature of Geography. 4th printing. Photo-Lithoprint. Ann Arbor (Mich.), 1951.

HARTSHORNE, R. (b), Perspective on the Nature of Geography. Chicago, 1959.

HARTSHORNE, R. and DICKEN, S. N. (a). A Classification of the Agricultural Regions of Europe and North America on a Uniform Statistical Basis. Annals of the Association of American Geographers, XXV (1935). pp. 99—120.

HARTSHORNE, R. and DICKEN, S. N. (b). Syllabus in Economic Geography. (Lithoprint). Ann Arbor (Mich.), 1938.

HETTNER, A. (a). Die Geographie. Ihre Geschichte, ihr Wesen und ihre Methoden. Breslau, 1927.

HETTNER, A. (b). Vergleichende Länderkunde. Bd. I—IV. Leipzig-Berlin, 1933—1935.

HOLLANDER, A. N. J. DEN. Mens, Aarde en Wereldhuishouding. In: E.N.S.I.E. Vol. V. De Aarde. pp. 239—281, 343—357, 387—399.

HOOGVELD, J. H. E. J. (a). Inleiding tot de Wijsbegeerte. Vol. I. Beginselen van de Wetenschapsleer. 1st printing. Bois-le-Duc, 1933.

HOOGVELD, J. H. E. J. (b). Inleiding tot de Wijsbegeerte. Vol. I, 4th printing, revised by Dr. F. Sassen. Utrecht-Nijmegen, 1947.

HÖZEL, E. Das geographische Individuum bei Karl Ritter und seine Bedeutung für den Begriff des Naturgebietes und der Naturgrenze. Geographische Zeitschrift, II (1896) pp. 378—396; 433—444.

HUMBOLDT, A. VON. Kosmos. Bd. II. Stuttgart, 1847.

HUNTINGTON, E. Civilisation and Climate. 3rd revised ed. New Haven-London, 1924.

HUNTINGTON, E. and CUSHING, W. Principles of human geography. 6th ed. revised by B. Shaw. New York-London, 1953.

JAMES, P. E. See: American Geography. Inventory and Prospect.

JAMES, P. E. Introduction: The Field of Geography. In: American Geography. Inventory and Prospect. Syracuse, 1954. pp. 3—18.

JONES, C. F. See: American Geography. Inventory and Prospect.

JONES, E. Cause and Effect in Human Geography. Annals of the Association of American Geographers. XLVI (1956). pp. 369—377.

JONG, G. DE. (a). Het karakter van de geografische totaliteit. Groningen, 1955.

JONG, G. DE. (b). Denkvormen van het geografisch gebied in eenheid en verscheidenheid. (Inaugural lecture Free University, Amsterdam) Groningen 1955.

JONG, G. DE. (c). De geografische classificatie van het klimaat en Thornthwaite's klimaatsystemen. Tijdschrift voor Economische en Sociale Geografie, 48 (1957). pp. 20—30.

JONG, G. DE. (d). The Nature of Human Geography in the Light of the Ordinances of Creation. Free University Quarterly, V (1957—1958) pp. 97—119.

KEUNING, H. J. (a). Inleiding tot de sociale aardrijkskunde. Gorinchem, 1951.

KEUNING, H. J. (b). Mozaïek der functies. The Hague, 1955.

KEUNING, H. J. (c). Een halve eeuw Utrechtse sociale geografie. Tijdschrift Koninklijk Nederlands Aardrijkskundig Genootschap, LXXVI (1959). pp. 10—21.

KEUNING, H. J. (d). The Place of social Geography within human Geography. Tijdschrift Koninklijk Nederlands Aardrijkskundig Genootschap, LXXVII (1960). pp. 341—346.

KREBS, N. (a). Natur- und Kulturlandschaft. Zeitschrift der Gesellschaft für Erdkunde zu Berlin. 1923. pp. 81—94.

KREBS, N. (b). Question: Le concept Paysage dans la Géographie Humaine. Comptes rendus du congrès Internat. de Géographie Amsterdam 1938. Tome 2.

KREBS, N. (c). Vergleichende Länderkunde. 2. Auflage. Stuttgart, 1952.

KROEBER, A. L. History and Science in Anthropology. American Anthropologist. New Series. 37 (1935). pp. 539—569.

KUPERUS, G. Geografie als leer der bestaansruimte. Tijdschrift Koninklijk Nederlands Aardrijkskundig Genootschap, LXX (1953). pp. 488—505.

LANGEVELD, M. J. Op weg naar wijsgerig denken. 3e druk. Haarlem, 1951.

LE LANNOU, M. La géographie humaine. Paris, 1949.

LÜTGENS, R. See: Erde und Weltwirtschaft.

OTREMBA, E. See: Erde und Weltwirtschaft.

PAASSEN, CHR. VAN. Carl Ritter anno 1959. Tijdschrift Koninklijk Nederlands Aardrijkskundig Genootschap, LXXVI (1959). pp. 327—351.

PAFFEN, K. Die natürliche Landschaft und ihre räumliche Gliederung. Remagen, 1953.

PASSARGE, S. Landeskunde und Vergleichende Landschaftskunde. Zeitschrift der Gesellschaft für Erdkunde zu Berlin. 1924. pp. 331—337.

PLEWE, E. (a). Untersuchung über den Begriff der Vergleichenden Erdkunde u.s.w. Zeitschrift der Gesellschaft für Erdkunde zu Berlin. 1932. Erg. Heft IV. pp. 28—46.

PLEWE, E. (b). Vom Wesen und den Methoden der regionalen Geographie. Studium Generale. V. Berlin etc. 1952. pp. 410—421.

POLSPOEL, G. Waarheen met de geographie? Mededelingen van de Koninklijke Vlaamse Academie voor Wetenschappen, Letteren en Schone Kunsten van België. Klasse der Wetenschappen. Vol. XX, 3. Brussels, 1958. pp. 3—41.

RICHTHOFEN, F. VON. Aufgaben und Methoden der heutigen Geographie. Antrittsrede Univ. Leipzig. Leipzig, 1883.

RICKERT, H. (a). Die Grenzen der naturwissenschaftlichen Begriffsbildung. 3/4. Auflage. Tübingen, 1921.

RICKERT, H. (b). Kulturwissenschaft und Naturwissenschaft. 6/7. Auflage. Tübingen, 1926.

RITTER, C. Einleitung zur allgemeinen vergleichenden Geographie, und Abhandlungen zur Begründung einer mehr wissenschaftlichen Behandlung der Erdkunde. Berlin, 1852.

SCHÄFER, F. K. Exceptionalism in Geography. A methodological Examination. Annals of the Association of American Geographers. XLIII (1953), pp. 226—249.

SCHMITHÜSEN, J. „Fliesengefüge der Landschaft" und „Ökotop". Vorschläge zur begrifflichen Ordnung und Nomenklatur in der Landschaftsforschung. Berichte zur deutschen Landeskunde, V (1948). pp. 74—83. (a).

SCHMITTHENNER, H. (a). Zum Problem der Allgemeinen Geographie. Geographica Helvetica, VI (1951). pp. 123—137.

SCHMITTHENNER, H. (b). Studien über Carl Ritter. Frankfurter Geographische Hefte. Heft 4. Frankfurt, 1951.

SCHMITTHENNER, H. (c). Zum Problem der Allgemeinen Geographie und der Länderkunde. Münchner Geographische Hefte. Heft 4. Kallmünz-Regensburg, 1954.

SORRE, M. Les fondements de la Géographie humaine. Vol. I, II (1,2), III. 1e—3e éd. Paris, 1948—1952.

STEBBING, L. S. (a). A Modern Elementary Logic. 5th ed. Revised by C. W. K. Mundle. London, 1957.

STEBBING, L. S. (b). A Modern Introduction to Logic. 7 th ed. repr. London, 1958.

TAYLOR, G. See: Geography in the Twentieth Century.

THORNTHWAITE, C. W. (a). The Climates of North America according to a new Classification. Geographical Review, XXI (1931). pp. 633—655.

THORNTHWAITE, C. W. (b). The Climates of the Earth. Geographical Review, XXIII (1933). pp. 433—440.

THORNTHWAITE, C. W. (c). An Approach toward a Rational Classification of Climate. Geographical Review, XXXVIII (1948). pp. 55—94.

TROLL, C. Die Geographische Landschaft und ihre Erforschung. Studium Generale, III. Berlin etc. 1950. pp. 162—181.

ULLMAN, E. L. Human Geography and area research. Annals of the Association of American Geographers, XLIII (1953). pp. 54—66.

UNSTEAD, J. F. A System of Regional Geography. Geography, 18 (1933). pp. 175—187.

VALK, J. G. VAN DER. Ernst Kapp. Diss. Utrecht, 1939.

VAN DALE. See Dale, van.

VAN DEN BERG, I. J. M. See Berg, I. J. M. van den.

VAN PAASSEN, CHR. See Paassen, Chr. van.

VERSTEGE, J. C. W. Geografie, regionaal onderzoek en geografische ordening. Diss. Utrecht, 1942.

VIDAL DE LA BLACHE, P. (a). Des caractères distinctifs de la géographie, Annales de géographie. XXII (1913). pp. 289—299.

VIDAL DE LA BLACHE, P. (b). Principles of human geography. Ed. by E. de Martonne. Transl. by M. Todd Bingham. Reprint. London 1950.

212

VOOYS, A. C. DE. De ontwikkeling van de sociale geografie in Nederland. (Inaugural lecture, University of Utrecht) Groningen, 1950.

VRIES, E. DE. De aarde betaalt. The Hague, 1948.

WEIZSÄCKER, C. F. VON. Beitrag zur Diskussion über Kausalität. Studium Generale, II. Berlin etc. 1949. pp. 126—129.

WESTEN. Het —— en Overig Nederland. Publ. Rijksdienst voor het Nationale Plan. The Hague, 1956.

WHITTLESEY, D. (a). Major Agricultural Regions of the Earth. Annals of the Association of American Geographers, XXVI (1936). pp. 199—240.

WHITTLESEY, D. (b). The regional concept and the regional method. In: American Geography. Inventory and Prospect. Syracuse, 1954. pp. 19—68.

WINDELBAND, W. Präludien. Bd. II. 6. Auflage. Tübingen, 1919.

WINKLER, E. Zur Frage der allgemeinen Geographie. Athenaeums-Schriften. Heft 2. Zürich, 1938.

WOOLDRIDGE, S. W. and EAST, W. G. The Spirit and Purpose of Geography. Revised and enlarged ed. London, 1958.

ZIMMERMANN, E. W. World Resources and Industries. Revised ed. New York, 1951.

ECHÉ

DATE DUE

OCT
OCT ~~2~~
MAR 1

JAN
FE

MAR
APR